TEACHER EDITION

Printed in U.S.A.

ISBN 978-0-547-59244-2

12 13 14 15 16 17 18 19 20 0877 21 20 19 18 17 16 15 14 13

4500429357   C D E F G

HOUGHTON MIFFLIN HARCOURT

 **CRITICAL AREA**

Critical Area 2
Geometry and Positions

COMMON CORE | **CRITICAL AREA** Describing shapes and space

> **Domain: Geometry**   CC.K.G

Lessons | **Grade K Common Core State Standards**

**9.1, 9.3, 9.5,
9.7, 9.9**

Identify and describe shapes (squares, circles, triangles, rectangles, hexagons, cubes, cones, cylinders, and spheres).
CC.K.G.2   Correctly name shapes regardless of their orientations or overall size.

**9.2, 9.4, 9.6,
9.8, 9.10, 9.11**

Analyze, compare, create, and compose shapes.
CC.K.G.4   Analyze and compare two- and three-dimensional shapes, in different sizes and orientations, using informal language to describe their similarities, differences, parts (e.g., number of sides and vertices/"corners") and other attributes (e.g., having sides of equal length).

9.12

Analyze, compare, create, and compose shapes.
CC.K.G.6   Compose simple shapes to form larger shapes.

Table of Contents

Geometry and Positions

Chapter 9 Identify and Describe Two-Dimensional Shapes

 COMMON CORE

Domain:
Geometry CC.K.G

 PROFESSIONAL DEVELOPMENT

Mathematical Practices:

CC.K–12.MP.3 Construct viable arguments and critique the reasoning of others.

CC.K–12.MP.7 Look for and make use of structure.

Planning

Lessons

* This chapter also includes the following standards: CC.K.G.3, CC.K.G.5

Geometry and Positions

COMMON CORE

CRITICAL AREA Describing shapes and space

Chapter 10

Identify and Describe Three-Dimensional Shapes . . . 409

Domain: Geometry

COMMON CORE
PROFESSIONAL DEVELOPMENT

See Teaching for Depth, pp. 353E and 409E

See Mathematical Practices, pp. 397A, 403, 433A, and 439

Geometry and Positions 345B

Digital Path

1 PLAN

● eTeacher Edition

- Access all Teacher Edition pages at school or home

● Chapter ePlanner

- Daily Digital Path links to all online resources for each lesson
- Create customized planning calendar
- View and assign online activities and lessons to students

● Professional Development Video Podcasts

- Download video podcasts with strategies for teaching concepts and skills
- View on hand-held device or computer

2 ENGAGE

● iTools

- Solve problems with interactive digital manipulatives
- Model and explore lesson math concepts

● HMH Mega Math

- Provides additional lesson practice with engaging activities that include audio and animation

3 TEACH

● eStudent Edition

- Includes all Student Edition pages for student access at school or home
- Provides audio reinforcement for each lesson
- Features point-of-use links to Animated Math Models

● Multimedia *eGlossary*

- Includes audio, graphics, and animation

● Animated Math Models

- Curious George introduces interactive lesson activities with audio and animation
- Concepts are modeled and reinforced with feedback

4 ASSESS

● Online Assessment System

- Receive instant results, including prescriptions for intervention
- Includes a variety of reports to track student progress
- Create customized tests

RtI Response to Intervention

● Soar to Success Math

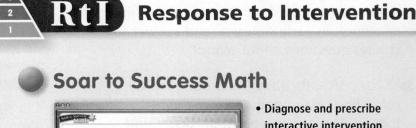

- Diagnose and prescribe interactive intervention lessons for all RtI Tiers

Tier 1 On-Level Intervention

Tier 2 Strategic Intervention

Tier 3 Intensive Intervention

21ST CENTURY SKILLS

Go Math! Digital Path provides the opportunity for lifelong learning skills for students in the 21st Century by developing:

- Information and communication skills
- Higher order thinking skills
- Problem solving skills
- Independent learners
- Real-world connections

1 READ

School Fun

Objective Use attributes such as size, color, and shape to determine similarities and differences.

Genre Nonfiction

Domain: Geometry

▶ **Preparing to Read** Refer children to the story cover and read the title. Ask what they think the book will be about.

Explain that they will read the story together, using the pictures to solve math problems on each page. Then they will read the story again, learn some fun facts about the history of schools in early America, and answer social studies questions about school.

▶ **Story Vocabulary** classroom, learning, rules, book bags, names, same, books, big, small, markers, colors, blocks, round, square, share

▶ **Reading the Math Story**

Pages 345–348

Discuss the school items shown on each page and how some items are the same and how some are different.

- **How can you tell which book bags are the same?** Two of the book bags are the same color and shape.
- **How are the big and small books alike?** They are all books. They all have four sides.
- **How are they different?** They are different sizes.

Discuss some rules in your classroom and why they are needed. Talk about the things that help keep your classroom running smoothly, such as taking turns, helping others, cleaning up, and sharing.

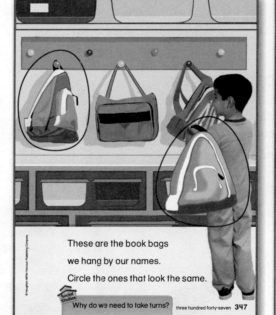

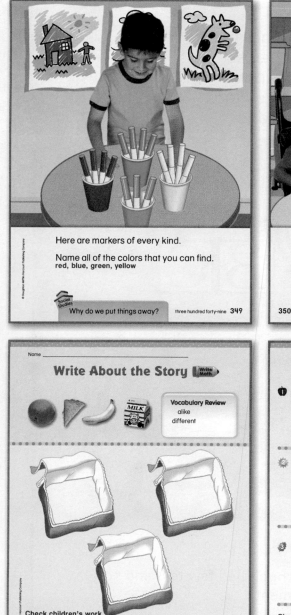

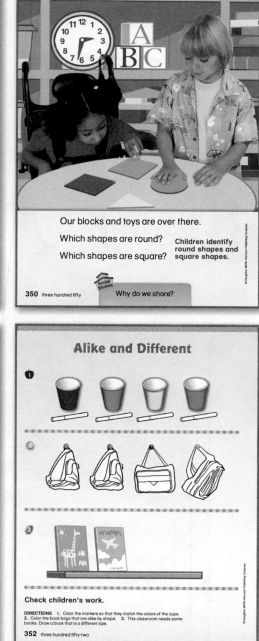

Children should understand the story progression. Have them share how they solved each problem.

- **How are the markers the same? How are they different?** They are all the same shape and size. They are different colors.

- **On the next page, how can you tell which shapes are round and which are square?** I know that round shapes are curved. I know that square shapes have four vertices and four straight sides.

2 RESPOND

Write About the Story

Page 351

Brainstorm ideas for food that children like and can draw in one of the lunch boxes. Point out the foods at the top of the page as examples. When children have finished, ask which lunch box is different now and why. Make sure that children understand that drawing food in one lunch box makes the lunch box different.

You may wish to have volunteers share their pictures with the class.

Math Vocabulary alike, different

Do the Math • Alike and Different

Page 352

In this activity, children continue to explore the ideas of *alike* and *different*.

 **Connections to Social Studies**

Read the story again as children follow along. Many of the items on the pages have been a part of the lives of schoolchildren for a long time. However, these items have changed over the years. For each page, tell children one of the following facts, which describe school life in this country a century or more ago. Have children look at the story pictures again and discuss the Social Studies question on each page.

SCHOOLHOUSE Fact:

- Long ago, a bell on top of one-room schoolhouses rang to tell children that it was time for class.

PLAYGROUND Facts:

- Children in early schools had few toys and no playground equipment.

- Instead of playing on the playground, children made up games or played games that children still play today, such as hide-and-seek and hopscotch.

BOOK BAG Facts:

- Long ago, children did not use book bags.

- Instead, each child wrapped a leather strap that looked similar to a belt around books to carry them from home.

CHALKBOARD Facts:

- In schools long ago, each child had a small board made of slate.

- Children wrote on their slates with pieces of chalk.

- These children had no papers or pencils for writing, and they did not keep their work.

LUNCH BOX Facts:

- Children once brought their lunch to school in tin pails or baskets.

- Inside might be some things that children today would recognize, such as sandwiches and apples.

The Project

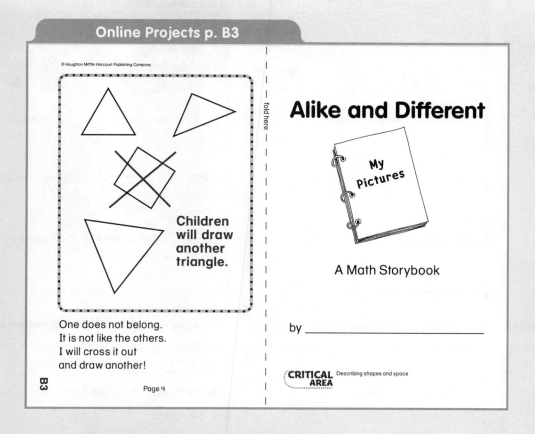

© Houghton Mifflin Harcourt Publishing Company

Children will draw another triangle.

One does not belong.
It is not like the others.
I will cross it out
and draw another!

B3 Page 4

Alike and Different

My Pictures

A Math Storybook

by _____

CRITICAL AREA Describing shapes and space

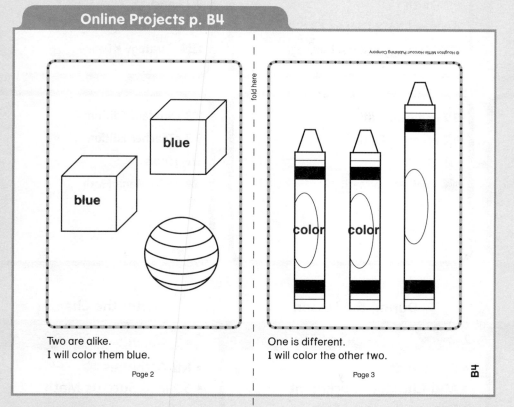

blue

blue

Two are alike.
I will color them blue.

Page 2

© Houghton Mifflin Harcourt Publishing Company

color color

One is different.
I will color the other two.

Page 3 B4

My Math Storybook

Alike and Different

Objective Use color, size, and shape to determine how objects are alike and how they are different.

Materials Online Projects pp. B3–B4, crayons

Help children fold their pages to make a storybook. Read each page of the storybook as children follow along. Explain to children that they will draw and color pictures to show how objects are alike or how they are different.

Once children have completed the pages, have them turn back to their storybook covers. Encourage each child to draw a picture that tells about his or her story. For example, a child might draw two objects that are alike in some way.

Have children work together and then share their work with the class. Children may take their storybooks home to share with family members.

 You may suggest that children place completed Projects in their portfolios.

Chapter At A Glance

Domain: Geometry

Chapter Essential Question How can you identify, name, and describe two-dimensional shapes?

Use the Chapter Planner in the *Go Math! Planning Guide* for pacing.

Lesson At A Glance	LESSON 9.1 CC.K.G.2 Identify and Name Circles 357A	LESSON 9.2 CC.K.G.4 Describe Circles 361A	LESSON 9.3 CC.K.G.2 Identify and Name Squares 365A
Essential Question	How can you identify and name circles?	How can you describe circles?	How can you identify and name squares?
Objective	Identify and name two-dimensional shapes including circles.	Describe attributes of circles.	Identify and name two-dimensional shapes including squares.
Vocabulary	**circle, two-dimensional shapes**	**curve**, circle	**corners, sides, square, vertex, vertices,** two-dimensional shapes
Materials	MathBoard, two-dimensional shapes, Counting Tape	MathBoard, Counting Tape	MathBoard, two-dimensional shapes, Counting Tape

Print Resources

9.1 Student Edition **9.1 Standards Practice Book** 9.1 Reteach **9.1 Enrich** **Grab-and-Go™ Centers Kit** **ELL** Strategy • Draw	**9.2 Student Edition** **9.2 Standards Practice Book** 9.2 Reteach **9.2 Enrich** **Grab-and-Go™ Centers Kit** **ELL** Strategy • Model Language	**9.3 Student Edition** **9.3 Standards Practice Book** 9.3 Reteach **9.3 Enrich** **Grab-and-Go™ Centers Kit** **ELL** Strategy • Define

Digital Path

9.1 eStudent Edition **9.1 eTeacher Edition** *iT* iTools HMH Mega Math	**9.2 eStudent Edition** **9.2 eTeacher Edition** *iT* iTools HMH Mega Math	**9.3 eStudent Edition** **9.3 eTeacher Edition** *iT* iTools HMH Mega Math

RtI — Response to Intervention

Before the Chapter	During the Lesson	After the Chapter
✓ **Show What You Know**	✓ **Share and Show**	✓ **Chapter Review/Test**
• **Prerequisite Skills Activities** • **Soar to Success Math**	• **RtI Activities** • **Mid-Chapter Checkpoint** • **Soar to Success Math**	• **RtI Activities** • **Soar to Success Math**

EVERY DAY
COUNTS®

Use every day to develop computational fluency.
Visit www.greatsource.com/everydaycounts

Assess Depth of Knowledge

See Chapter 9 Performance Task and
Assessment Guide.

LESSON 9.4 CC.K.G.4

**Describe
Squares** 369A

How can you describe squares?

Describe attributes of squares.

sides of equal length, corners, sides,
square, vertex, vertices

MathBoard, two-color counters,
Counting Tape

9.4 Student Edition
9.4 Standards Practice Book
9.4 Reteach
9.4 Enrich
Grab-and-Go™ Centers Kit
ELL **Strategy** • Model Language

9.4 eStudent Edition
9.4 eTeacher Edition
*i*T *i*Tools
MM HMH Mega Math

LESSON 9.5 CC.K.G.2

**Identify and Name
Triangles** 373A

How can you identify and name triangles?

Identify and name two-dimensional
shapes including triangles.

triangle, two-dimensional shapes

MathBoard, two-dimensional shapes,
Counting Tape

9.5 Student Edition
9.5 Standards Practice Book
9.5 Reteach
9.5 Enrich
Grab-and-Go™ Centers Kit
ELL **Strategy** • Describe

9.5 eStudent Edition
9.5 eTeacher Edition
*i*T *i*Tools
MM HMH Mega Math

LESSON 9.6 CC.K.G.4

**Describe
Triangles** 377A

How can you describe triangles?

Describe attributes of triangles.

corners, sides, triangle, vertex, vertices

MathBoard, two-color counters,
Counting Tape

9.6 Student Edition
9.6 Standards Practice Book
9.6 Reteach
9.6 Enrich
Grab-and-Go™ Centers Kit
ELL **Strategy** • Rephrase

9.6 eStudent Edition
9.6 eTeacher Edition
*i*T *i*Tools
MM HMH Mega Math

**GREAT ON
INTERACTIVE
WHITEBOARD**

Digital Path

- Animated Math Models
- ✓ Assessment
- MM HMH Mega Math
- *i*T *i*Tools
- ABC Multimedia *e*Glossary
- 📱 Professional Development
  Video Podcasts
- Soar to Success Math

Chapter At A Glance

Domain: Geometry

Lesson At A Glance

	LESSON 9.7 CC.K.G.2	**LESSON 9.8** CC.K.G.4	**LESSON 9.9** CC.K.G.2
	Identify and Name Rectangles 381A	**Describe Rectangles 385A**	**Identify and Name Hexagons 389A**
Essential Question	How can you identify and name rectangles?	How can you describe rectangles?	How can you identify and name hexagons?
Objective	Identify and name two-dimensional shapes including rectangles.	Describe attributes of rectangles.	Identify and name two-dimensional shapes including hexagons.
Vocabulary	**rectangle**, sides of equal length, two-dimensional shapes	rectangle, sides, sides of equal length, vertex, vertices, corners	**hexagon**, two-dimensional shapes
Materials	MathBoard, two-dimensional shapes, Counting Tape	MathBoard, two-color counters, Counting Tape	MathBoard, two-dimensional shapes, Counting Tape

Print Resources

9.7	9.8	9.9
9.7 Student Edition	**9.8 Student Edition**	**9.9 Student Edition**
9.7 Standards Practice Book	**9.8 Standards Practice Book**	**9.9 Standards Practice Book**
9.7 Reteach	9.8 Reteach	9.9 Reteach
9.7 Enrich	**9.8 Enrich**	**9.9 Enrich**
Grab-and-Go™ Centers Kit	**Grab-and-Go™ Centers Kit**	**Grab-and-Go™ Centers Kit**
ELL Strategy • Model Concepts	**ELL Strategy** • Identify Relationships	**ELL Strategy** • Draw

Digital Path

9.7	9.8	9.9
9.7 *e*Student Edition	**9.8 *e*Student Edition**	**9.9 *e*Student Edition**
9.7 *e*Teacher Edition	**9.8 *e*Teacher Edition**	**9.9 *e*Teacher Edition**
iT **iTools**	*iT* **iTools**	*iT* **iTools**
HMH Mega Math	**HMH Mega Math**	**HMH Mega Math**

Assessment

Diagnostic	Formative	Summative
• **Show What You Know**	• **Lesson Quick Check**	• **Chapter Review/Test**
• **Diagnostic Interview Task**	• **Mid-Chapter Checkpoint**	• **Performance Assessment**
• **Soar to Success Math**		• **Chapter Test**
		• **Online Assessment**

LESSON 9.10 CC.K.G.4

Describe Hexagons 393A

How can you describe hexagons?

Describe attributes of hexagons.

corners, hexagon, sides, vertex, vertices

MathBoard, two-color counters, Counting Tape

9.10 Student Edition
9.10 Standards Practice Book
9.10 Reteach
9.10 Enrich
Grab-and-Go™ Centers Kit
ELL **Strategy** • Model Language

9.10 *e*Student Edition
9.10 *e*Teacher Edition
*i*T *i*Tools
MM HMH Mega Math

LESSON 9.11 CC.K.G.4

Hands On: Algebra • Compare Two-Dimensional Shapes 397A

How can you use the words *alike* and *different* to compare two-dimensional shapes?

Use the words *alike* and *different* to compare two-dimensional shapes by attributes.

alike, **different**, two-dimensional shapes

MathBoard, two-dimensional shapes, Counting Tape

9.11 Student Edition
9.11 Standards Practice Book
9.11 Reteach
9.11 Enrich
Grab-and-Go™ Centers Kit
ELL **Strategy** • Describe

9.11 *e*Student Edition
9.11 *e*Teacher Edition
Animated Math Models
*i*T *i*Tools
MM HMH Mega Math

LESSON 9.12 CC.K.G.6

Problem Solving • Draw to Join Shapes 401A

How can you solve problems using the strategy *draw a picture*?

Solve problems by using the strategy *draw a picture*.

MathBoard, pattern blocks, Counting Tape

9.12 Student Edition
9.12 Standards Practice Book
9.12 Reteach
9.12 Enrich
Grab-and-Go™ Centers Kit
ELL **Strategy** • Model Language

9.12 *e*Student Edition
9.12 *e*Teacher Edition
✓ Chapter 9 Test
Animated Math Models
MM HMH Mega Math

Teaching for Depth

by Thomasenia Lott Adams
Professor of Mathematics Education
University of Florida
Gainesville, Florida

Spatial Sense

A primary aim of engaging learners in the study of two-dimensional shapes is to develop their spatial sense.

- Spatial sense is "an intuition about shapes and the relationships among shapes" (Van de Walle, 2007, p. 408).

- Such intuition can be supported by giving children experiences with naming, describing, and sorting shapes.

- Being able to talk about shapes and their characteristics is an indicator of spatial sense. An example is describing shapes by the number of vertices and sides.

Vocabulary

When children are exposed to shapes, they will use vocabulary that is accessible to them.

- When children describe a triangle as having "three points," introducing the formal vocabulary of *vertex* will help them transition to using the formal language of geometry.

- Modeling the use of the formal vocabulary informs children without discrediting the development that they have reached by using their own informal vocabulary.

Recognizing Attributes to Sort

It is important to provide opportunities to develop language to help children classify and describe objects.

From the Research

" ...[L]earning the characteristic properties of a geometrical shape is essential because they can form the basis of higher levels of thinking and help in gaining a practical and intuitive grasp of the mathematics of space."

(Triadafillidis, 1995, p. 225)

COMMON CORE Mathematical Practices

Geometry is the perfect mathematical content to empower children to **model with mathematics**. For example, young children can select geometric shapes to represent objects they see in the classroom or their home environments (e.g., a rectangle may represent a picture frame or the bricks on the school walls). When they consider the characteristics of mathematical models they may ask questions such as, "Why are circles better models for bicycle tires than triangles?" This examination of characteristics enhances their understanding of the shape.

PODCASTING

Professional Development Video Podcast: Measurement and Geometry, Grades K–2, Segment 2

Cross-Curricular Center Activities

Social Studies Center

Shapes in Signs

Objective Children recognize shapes in safety signs.

Materials pictures of safety signs in octagon, rectangle, square, triangle, and circle shapes, Two-Dimensional Shapes (see *eTeacher Resources*)

- Provide children with pictures of traffic signs, such as a stop sign, railroad crossing sign, yield sign, and crosswalk sign. Discuss how these kinds of signs help keep people safe.
- Provide two-dimensional shapes and have partners locate those that are the same shape as some of the signs.
- Have children trace the shapes and write or dictate the safety message that is usually seen on each sign.

STOP

Art Center

Picture This

Objective Children use a variety of two-dimensional shapes to create pictures of real objects.

Materials two-dimensional construction-paper shapes in various sizes, paste or glue

- Display a square, rectangle, and triangle. **What shapes are these? I can make a picture of a house by combining these two shapes.** Paste the shapes together to make a house.
- Identify two-dimensional shapes by asking questions such as the following: **Which shape did I use for the roof? Which shape did I use for the door?**
- Have children create pictures of objects using different shapes.

Technology Center

Cut and Paste Shapes

Objective Use a computer to explore two-dimensional shapes.

Materials computer, printer

- In advance, scan in or create a document with a large circle, rectangle, triangle, and square. Label the shapes.
- Demonstrate the "save as" feature to children.
- Each partner takes a turn saving the document, typing his or her name on it, and printing out the page.
- Children color the printed shapes.

Review Prerequisite Skills

 RtI

Activities

Numbers of Shapes — TIER 2

Objective Review numbers through 8 and shape names.

Materials Number and Symbol Tiles (front), Two-Dimensional Shapes (see *eTeacher Resources*)

Use number tiles 1 to 8, and have children work in pairs. The first child should choose a number tile for the other to read, and then show or name a shape. The partner should display the number tile and that number of shapes.

The first child should then ask the partner to state the number and name the shape. Children can change roles and repeat the activity.

As children work, circulate and ask questions such as the following:

- **What shape are you showing?**
- **How did you know how many to show?**
- **What number does your tile show?**
- **What can you tell about these shapes?**

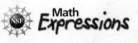 **Math Expressions** Model from *Math Expressions*. For more information visit **www.eduplace.com/hmhschool/mathexpressions**

Sort by Shape — TIER 2

Objective Review sorting by shape.

Materials Two-Dimensional Shapes (see *eTeacher Resources*)

Hold up a small red rectangle and ask children to describe it. Repeat this process for a big green circle, a small red triangle, and a big blue square.

- **You can notice at least three things about the shapes—their color, size, and shape.**
- **If you put them in sets or sort them by shape, how many sets will you make?** 4

Have pairs work together to sort by shape. As children work, ask questions such as the following:

- **What is the name of this set?**
- **How do you know this one belongs in this set?**
- **How are all the shapes in this set the same?**
- **How are they different?**

 Common Core State Standards Across the Grades

Before	Grade K	After
• Recognize, name, and describe a circle, square, triangle, and rectangle. • Sort and classify by one attribute.	**Domain: Geometry** Identify and describe shapes (squares, circles, triangles, rectangles, hexagons, cubes, cones, cylinders, and spheres). **CC.K.G.2** Analyze, compare, create, and compose shapes. **CC.K.G.4, CC.K.G.6**	**Domain: Geometry** Reason with shapes and their attributes. **CC.1.G.1, CC.1.G.2, CC.1.G.3**

See A page of each lesson for Common Core Standard text.

Developing Math Language

Chapter Vocabulary

alike the same

circle a plane curve equidistant from the center

curve a line that is rounded

different not the same

hexagon a two-dimensional, or flat, shape with 6 straight sides and 6 vertices

rectangle a two-dimensional, or flat, shape with 4 straight sides and 4 square vertices

sides the line segments that form a polygon

square a two-dimensional, or flat, shape with 4 straight sides of equal length and 4 square vertices

triangle a two-dimensional, or flat, shape with 3 straight sides and 3 vertices

vertex, corner the point where two sides of a polygon meet

vertices used to name more than one vertex

GO Online Multimedia eGlossary

ELL Vocabulary Activity

Objective Understand the math terms *vertex* and *vertices*.

Materials Vocabulary Cards for *vertex* and *vertices*, Pattern Blocks (see *eTeacher Resources*)

Place several different pattern blocks on the table. Hold up a triangle. Point to one vertex of the triangle and explain that the corner of a triangle is called a *vertex*. Then point to all three corners and explain that when talking about more than one vertex, the word *vertices* is used. Have children repeat each vocabulary term. Have children identify the vertices of the other pattern blocks.

Practice vocabulary by using questioning such as:

Beginning
- Show children a square. **How many vertices does the square have?** 4

Intermediate
- **Which shape has 6 vertices?** hexagon

Advanced
- **How can you identify how many vertices a shape has?** Accept all reasonable responses.

See **ELL** Activity Guide for leveled activities.

Vocabulary Strategy • Word Wall

- Post new words that children may need to practice on the word wall as each lesson is introduced.
- Practice these words as a "warm up" activity before the lessons.
- When one of the words appears in the lesson, reinforce it by pointing to it on the word wall.

Add these words onto the word wall.

alike	sides
circle	square
corner	triangle
curve	two-dimensional shapes
different	vertex
hexagon	vertices
rectangle	

side

vertex

Chapter 9

Introduce the Chapter

Curious About Math with Curious George

The sails on these boats are shaped like a triangle.

- **How many stripes can you count on the first sail?** 9

Additional facts about sailboats:

- **The pole that holds the sail is called a mast.**

- **Sailboats come in all different sizes.**

Ask the following questions to guide children to an answer.

- **How many sailboats do you see?** Accept reasonable answers.

- **What numbers do you see on the second sail?** 9, 6, 7, 2, 8

- **What colors do you see on the first sail?** blue, purple, red, yellow, orange, green, white

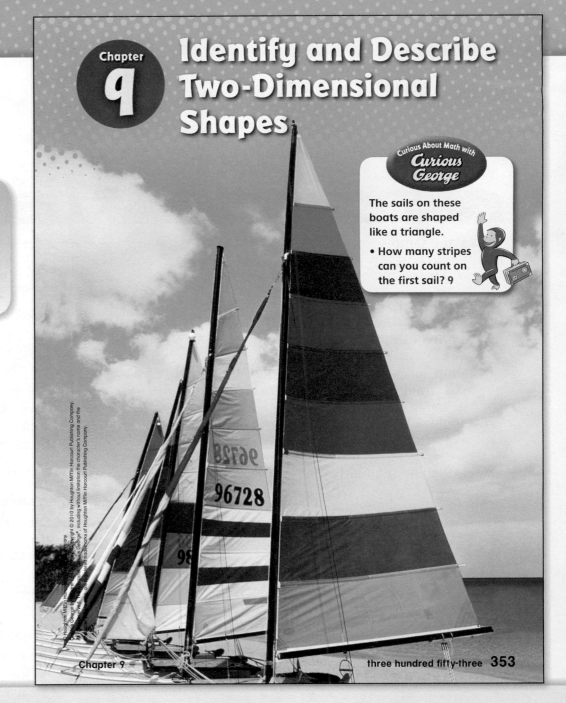

Chapter 9 Identify and Describe Two-Dimensional Shapes

Curious About Math with Curious George

The sails on these boats are shaped like a triangle.

- How many stripes can you count on the first sail? 9

96728

Chapter 9   three hundred fifty-three **353**

Intervention Options 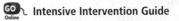 RtI Response to Intervention

Use Show What You Know, Lesson Quick Check, and Assessments to diagnose children's intervention levels.

TIER 1	TIER 2	TIER 3	ENRICHMENT
On-Level Intervention	**Strategic Intervention**	**Intensive Intervention**	**Independent Activities**
For children who are generally at grade level but need early intervention with the lesson concepts, use:	For children who need small group instruction to review concepts and skills needed for the chapter, use:	For children who need one-on-one instruction to build foundational skills for the chapter, use:	For children who successfully complete lessons, use:
▲ Tier 1 Activity for every lesson	▲ Tier 2 Activity for every lesson	GO Online Intensive Intervention Guide	 **Differentiated Centers Kit**
★ Soar to Success Math	GO Online Strategic Intervention Guide	★ Soar to Success Math	• Enrich Activity for every lesson
	▲ Prerequisite Skills Activities		• Enrich Book
	★ Soar to Success Math		MM HMH Mega Math

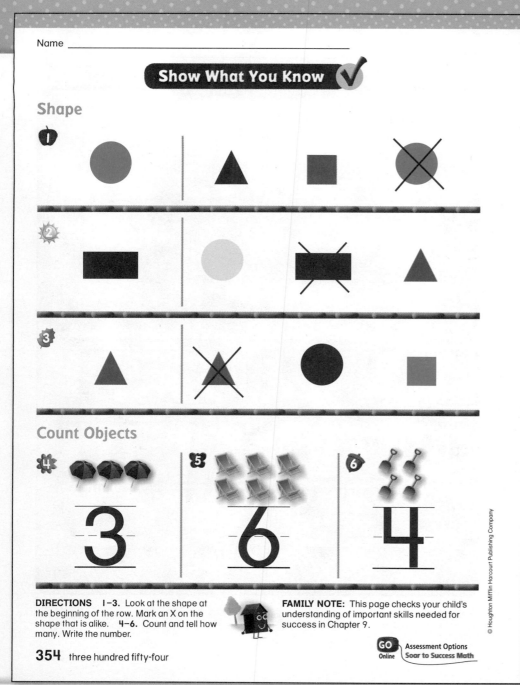

Show What You Know

Shape

①

②

③

Count Objects

④ 3

⑤ 6

⑥ 4

DIRECTIONS 1–3. Look at the shape at the beginning of the row. Mark an X on the shape that is alike. 4–6. Count and tell how many. Write the number.

FAMILY NOTE: This page checks your child's understanding of important skills needed for success in Chapter 9.

© Houghton Mifflin Harcourt Publishing Company

354 three hundred fifty-four

GO Online · Assessment Options · Soar to Success Math

Assessing Prior Knowledge

Have children complete on their own **Show What You Know.** Tested items are the prerequisite skills of this chapter.

Diagnostic Interview Task

The alternative interview tasks below evaluate children's understanding of each **Show What You Know** skill. The diagnostic chart may be used for intervention on prerequisite skills.

Materials Two-Dimensional Shapes (see *eTeacher Resources*), connecting cubes

For evaluation checklist see *Assessment Guide.*

- Give the child a variety of shapes. Show the child a circle. Have the child find a shape that is alike. Repeat the process with a triangle and then a square.
- Place five cubes on the table. Have the child count the cubes and write how many. Repeat the process using three cubes and then six cubes.

✔ Show What You Know • Diagnostic Assessment

Use to determine if children need intervention for the chapter's prerequisite skills.

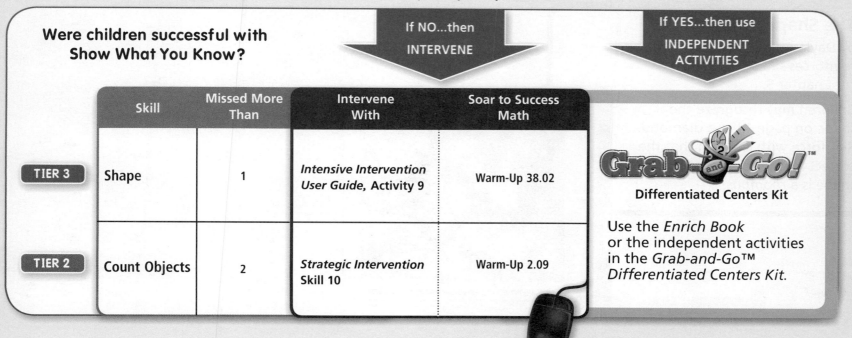

Were children successful with Show What You Know?

If NO...then INTERVENE

If YES...then use INDEPENDENT ACTIVITIES

	Skill	Missed More Than	Intervene With	Soar to Success Math
TIER 3	Shape	1	*Intensive Intervention User Guide,* Activity 9	Warm-Up 38.02
TIER 2	Count Objects	2	*Strategic Intervention* Skill 10	Warm-Up 2.09

Grab-and-Go!™
Differentiated Centers Kit

Use the *Enrich Book* or the independent activities in the *Grab-and-Go™ Differentiated Centers Kit.*

Vocabulary Builder

Children use multiple strategies to develop grade-appropriate vocabulary.

Have children complete the activities on the page by working alone or with partners.

Look at the page with children. Talk about and name the various fruits and vegetables.

- **Which fruits are red?** strawberries, apples
  Which fruits are yellow? lemons, bananas
- **How are the different fruits and vegetables sorted?** Accept reasonable answers.

Have children use color and shape words to describe the fruits and vegetables they see on the page.

Have children circle the box that is sorted by green vegetables. Then have children mark an X on the box that is sorted by purple fruit.

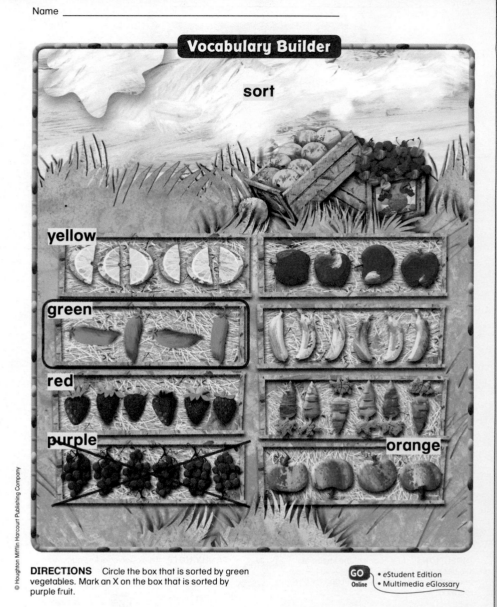

DIRECTIONS Circle the box that is sorted by green vegetables. Mark an X on the box that is sorted by purple fruit.

Chapter 9

three hundred fifty-five **355**

Literature Big Book

The Shape of Things

by Dayle Ann Dodds reinforces shape recognition for Chapter 9.

Children may recognize the shape on page 14 as a diamond. Reinforce with children that the correct mathematical term for this shape is a *rhombus*.

Chapter 9 **Game** Number Picture

DIRECTIONS Play with a partner. Decide who goes first. Toss the number cube. Color a shape in the picture that matches the number rolled. A player misses a turn if a number is rolled and all shapes with that number are colored. Continue until all shapes in the picture are colored.

MATERIALS number cube (labeled 1, 2, 2, 3, 3, 4), crayons

356 three hundred fifty-six

Game Number Picture

▶ Using the Game

Set up a game center in the classroom. Include the *Number Picture* game, along with the materials needed to play.

Materials number cube (1–4), crayons

Play with a partner. Decide who goes first. Toss the number cube. Color a shape in the picture that matches the number rolled.

A player misses a turn if a number is rolled and all matching shapes with that number are colored. Continue until all shapes in the picture are colored.

© Houghton Mifflin Harcourt Publishing Company

Standards Practice K.9

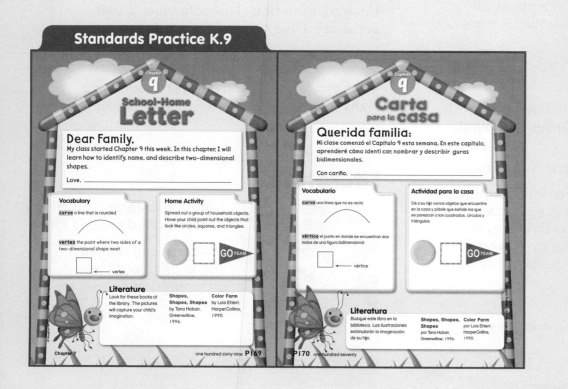

School-Home Letter available in English and Spanish in the *Standards Practice Book*, pp. P169–P170

The letter provides families with an overview of the math in the chapter, math vocabulary, an activity, and literature to read together.

Identify and Describe Two-Dimensional Shapes 356

Identify and Name Circles

LESSON AT A GLANCE

Common Core Standard
Identify and decribe shapes (squares, circles, triangles, rectangles, hexagons, cubes, cones, cylinders, and spheres).
CC.K.G.2 Correctly name shapes regardless of their orientations or overall size.

Also CC.K.G.3

Materials
MathBoard, two-dimensional shapes

Lesson Objective
Identify and name two-dimensional shapes including circles.

Essential Question
How can you identify and name circles?

Vocabulary circle, two-dimensional shapes

Digital Path

iT iTools: Geometry

HMH Mega Math

eStudent Edition

PROFESSIONAL DEVELOPMENT
COMMON CORE

About the Math

Teaching for Depth

A circle is defined as a closed curve lying in a plane, all points of which are equidistant from the center. A circle is not a polygon.

To add even more meaning to the name *circle,* you might use activities like these.

• Have children trace circles in the air as you say the following. **Trace around and around. Circles are round. Circles do not have straight parts.**

• Draw a circle and an oval. Help children compare them.

• Provide a piece of string about two yards long with a piece of chalk tied to one end. On a paved surface outdoors, let a child hold one end of the string on the ground while another child stretches the string and traces a shape—a circle—on the paved surface. Let children walk or skip around it.

 PODCASTING
Professional Development Video Podcasts

Daily Routines

Math Board

Common Core

SPIRAL REVIEW

 eTransparency
9.1

Problem of the Day

Calendar Math Name some numbers on the calendar that have all straight parts.

Name some numbers that have all curved parts.

Name some numbers that have both curved and straight parts. 1, 4, and 7 have straight parts. 3, 6, 8, 9 and 0 have curved parts. 2, 5, and sometimes 9 have both straight and curved parts.

CALENDAR Point to numbers on the calendar and lead children in saying them in order. Discuss the shapes of numerals on the calendar, pointing out the numerals as children talk about them.

Vocabulary Builder

Circle

Draw a circle and have children name and **describe it.** It is a circle; it is round or curved. It looks like a plate, wheel, or ring.

Have children find classroom objects that are shaped like circles. Possible answers: rim of wastebasket, outline of clock, plate, wheel rims of toys, bottoms of cups

• **What are some foods that are round like circles?** Possible answers: whole pizzas, pancakes, bagels, rice cakes

Literature

From the Grab-and-Go™ Differentiated Centers Kit

Children read the book and learn about the different shapes used to make a cart.

And the Wheels Go Round

Differentiated Instruction Activities

ELL Language Support
Kinesthetic · Small Group

Strategy: Draw

Children can demonstrate their understanding by drawing rather than by using language.

- Draw different size circles on the board.

- Have children identify the shapes and describe them. Possible answers: They are all circles; they are all round and flat; they are different sizes.

- Ask children to draw a picture of a snowman using different size circles.

- Repeat with another picture if time permits.

See **ELL** Activity Guide for leveled activities.

Enrich
Visual · Individual / Partners

Materials crayons, paper

Distribute crayons and a piece of paper to each child.

- Challenge children to draw a spider with eight legs using only circles. Remind them that they can use different sized circles in their picture.

- Have children trade their picture with a partner. Have each child count how many circles they find in the picture and write the number.

- Repeat the activity with other pictures, such as a table.

RtI Response to Intervention

Reteach Tier 1
Visual / Kinesthetic · Whole Class / Small Group

Materials everyday objects

Ask children to trace around different objects. For example, they might trace around a cup and a book.

- Point to one of the tracings. **Is this a circle or NOT a circle?**

Continue pointing to tracings and asking children to identify the shapes that are circles and the shapes that are not circles.

Tier 2
Visual / Kinesthetic · Small Group

Have the group stand up and hold hands in a circle. Tell children to step back, as far as they can.

- **What shape are we making?** circle

- Make sure children are in a circle and not an oval.

Discuss that all children should be exactly the same distance away from the center point.

When children take a step back, discuss how they must all move back the same distance.

- If there are enough children, split the group into smaller groups to make smaller circles.

① ENGAGE

Materials two-dimensional shapes

Access Prior Knowledge Invite children to explore shapes.

- **How could you sort the shapes?** by color, shape, or size

- **Decide how you want to sort. Then sort a handful of shapes.**

Have children share their sets and explain how they sorted them. Check visually.

② TEACH and TALK ⟨GO⟩ *iTools* Online

▶ **Listen and Draw** ⟨MATHEMATICAL PRACTICES⟩

Materials two-dimensional shapes

Read aloud this problem as children listen.

Jack has a sticker collection. He wants to sort the stickers into sets. One set will be circles. How will Jack know which stickers are circles?

Help children locate and read the word *circles*. Hold up a circle and trace around it with your finger, saying that it is a round and two-dimensional, or flat, shape.

Give children assorted two-dimensional shapes and have them sort out the circles, identifying and naming them as they do so. Children can also use the Two-Dimensional Shapes cutouts from the *eTeacher Resources* and glue them on the page.

- **Look at your shapes. Sort them on the mat into sets: *circles* and *not circles*. Trace and color them.**

- **How many shapes on the left of the sorting mat are circles?** all of the shapes

- **How many shapes on the right of the sorting mat are circles?** none of the shapes

- **What else can you say about a circle?** It is round and flat.

Reread the problem.

- **How will Jack know which stickers are circles?** He can find stickers that are round and flat.

COMMON CORE CC.K.G.2 Correctly name shapes regardless of their orientations or overall size.

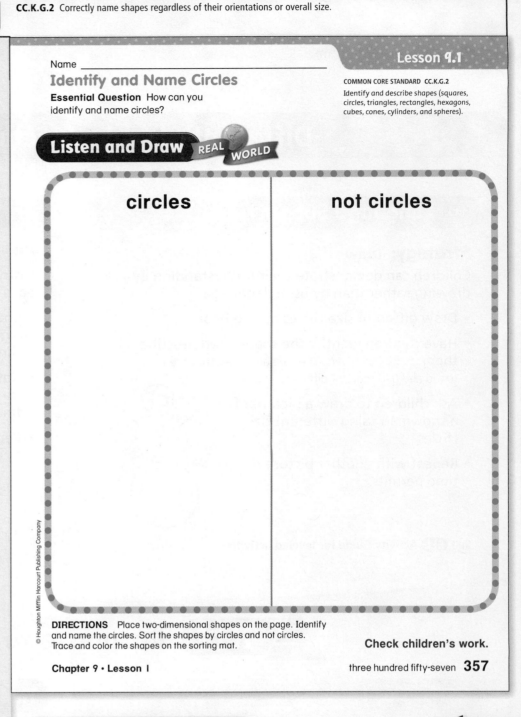

Name _____

Lesson 9.1

Identify and Name Circles

Essential Question How can you identify and name circles?

COMMON CORE STANDARD CC.K.G.2
Identify and describe shapes (squares, circles, triangles, rectangles, hexagons, cubes, cones, cylinders, and spheres).

Listen and Draw REAL WORLD

circles	not circles

© Houghton Mifflin Harcourt Publishing Company

DIRECTIONS Place two-dimensional shapes on the page. Identify and name the circles. Sort the shapes by circles and not circles. Trace and color the shapes on the sorting mat.

Check children's work.

Chapter 9 • Lesson 1

three hundred fifty-seven **357**

Standards Practice 9.1

Common Core

SPIRAL REVIEW

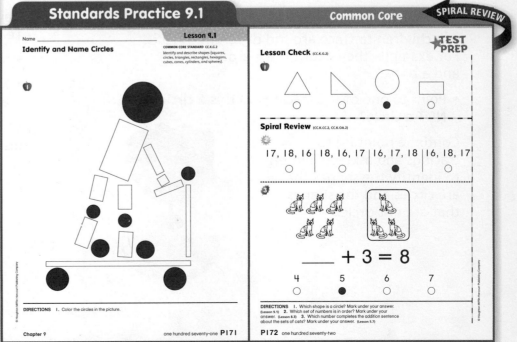

Name _____

Lesson 9.1

Identify and Name Circles

COMMON CORE STANDARD CC.K.G.2
Identify and describe shapes (squares, circles, triangles, rectangles, hexagons, cubes, cones, cylinders, and spheres).

Lesson Check (CC.K.G.2)

★TEST PREP

Spiral Review (CC.K.CC.2, CC.K.OA.2)

17, 18, 16 | 18, 16, 17 | 16, 17, 18 | 16, 18, 17

_____ + 3 = 8

4   5   6   7

DIRECTIONS 1. Color the circles in the picture.

DIRECTIONS 1. Which shape is a circle? Mark under your answer. (Lesson 9.1) 2. Which set of numbers is in order? Mark under your answer. (Lesson 8.3) 3. Which number completes the addition sentence about the sets of cats? Mark under your answer. (Lesson 5.7)

Chapter 9

one hundred seventy-one **P171**

P172 one hundred seventy-two

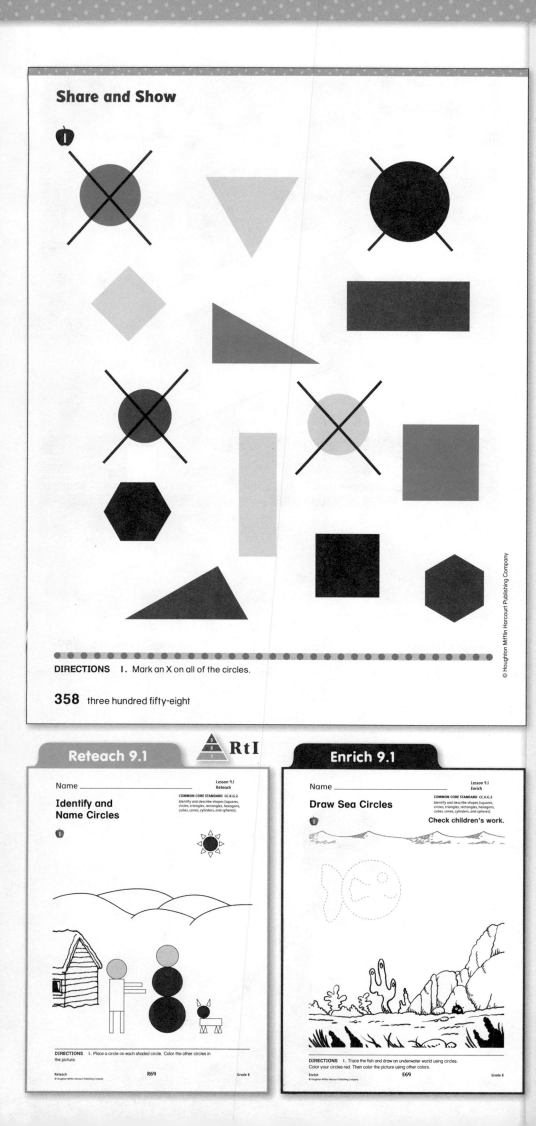

Share and Show

①

© Houghton Mifflin Harcourt Publishing Company

---

③ PRACTICE [Math Board]

▶ **Share and Show** • **Guided Practice**

- Look at the shapes on the page in Exercise 1. **Are all of the shapes the same?** no
- **Are any of the shapes circles?** yes
- **How do you know that they are circles?** They are round and flat.

Have children find all of the circles and then mark them with an X.

- **How many circles are on the page?** 4
- **Describe the circles.** Possible answers: The circles are round and flat. They are small, medium, and large. They are blue, yellow, green, and red.

Reteach 9.1 ▲ RtI

Name _____

Lesson 9.1
Reteach

Identify and Name Circles

COMMON CORE STANDARD CC.K.G.2
Identify and describe shapes (squares, circles, triangles, rectangles, hexagons, cubes, cones, cylinders, and spheres).

①

DIRECTIONS 1. Place a circle on each shaded circle. Color the other circles in the picture.

Reteach
© Houghton Mifflin Harcourt Publishing Company   R69   Grade K

Enrich 9.1

Name _____

Lesson 9.1
Enrich

Draw Sea Circles

COMMON CORE STANDARD CC.K.G.2
Identify and describe shapes (squares, circles, triangles, rectangles, hexagons, cubes, cones, cylinders, and spheres).

Check children's work.

①

DIRECTIONS 1. Trace the fish and draw an underwater world using circles. Color your circles red. Then color the picture using other colors.

Enrich
© Houghton Mifflin Harcourt Publishing Company   E69   Grade K

⚠ COMMON ERRORS

Error Children may have difficulty identifying circles.

Example Children name other shapes as circles.

Springboard to Learning Have children trace a circle. Establish that the circle is round and flat. With children, name things that are round like a circle such as a ring or hoop. Have them draw circles in the air or on a table using a finger.

▶ More Practice

Guide a discussion about the circles in the picture. Children may notice a circle is used to represent the head, and circles are used to represent the feet, elbows, and knees on the person in the picture.

• **Color the circles.**

• **How many circles did you color?** 7

Use Exercise 2 for **Quick Check.**

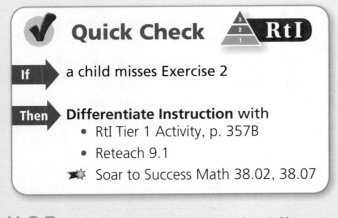

Quick Check

If ▶ a child misses Exercise 2

Then ▶ **Differentiate Instruction** with
  • RtI Tier 1 Activity, p. 357B
  • Reteach 9.1
  • Soar to Success Math 38.02, 38.07

H.O.T. Problem How are the circles different than the other shapes on the person in the picture? Possible answer: The circles are round. The other shapes are not round.

Go Deeper

Have children identify circles on a page in a picture book. Have each child describe the circles to a partner.

Name _____

© Houghton Mifflin Harcourt Publishing Company

DIRECTIONS 2. Color the circles in the picture.

Chapter 9 • Lesson 1   three hundred fifty-nine **359**

PROBLEM SOLVING

Check children's work.

DIRECTIONS 1. Which shape is a circle? Mark an X on that shape. **2.** Draw to show what you know about circles. Tell a friend about your drawing.

HOME ACTIVITY · Have your child show you an object that is shaped like a circle.

360 three hundred sixty

FOR MORE PRACTICE:
Standards Practice Book, pp. P171–P172

▶ **Problem Solving** (MATHEMATICAL PRACTICES)

Have children look at Exercise 1. Read the problem. Ask children to explain how they will solve the problem.

• **How many shapes do you see?** 5
• **Are they all circles?** no
• **How many circles do you see?** 1

Draw an oval and a circle. Explain that the oval looks like a "stretched out" or "squashed" circle. Tell children that it is not a circle; it is a shape called an oval.

• **Mark an X on the circle.** Check visually.

Before children draw to show what they know about a circle, ask them to tell what they know. Guide children to say that a circle is a round and flat shape. Have them tell a friend about their drawing.

④ SUMMARIZE (MATHEMATICAL PRACTICES)

Essential Question

How can you identify and name circles?
I know that a circle is round and flat.

Differentiated Instruction INDEPENDENT ACTIVITIES

Grab-and-Go!™
Differentiated Centers Kit

Literature
And the Wheels Go Round
Children read the book and learn about the different shapes used to make a cart.

Games
Follow the Figures
Children identify shapes to follow the game path to the end.

Digital Path

- Animated Math Models
- *i*Tools
- HMH Mega Math
- Soar to Success Math
- *e*Student Edition

Lesson 9.1 360

Describe Circles

LESSON AT A GLANCE

Common Core Standard
Analyze, compare, create, and compose shapes.
CC.K.G.4 Analyze and compare two- and three-dimensional shapes, in different sizes and orientations, using informal language to describe their similarities, differences, parts (e.g., number of sides and vertices/"corners") and other attributes (e.g., having sides of equal length).

Also CC.K.G.2, CC.K.G.5

Lesson Objective
Describe attributes of circles.

Essential Question
How can you describe circles?

Vocabulary curve

Materials
MathBoard

Digital Path
i**Ti**Tools: Geometry

GO eStudent Edition

MM HMH Mega Math

COMMON CORE PROFESSIONAL DEVELOPMENT
About the Math

If Children Ask

While discussing classroom objects that are shaped like circles, a child might show a ball and say, "This ball is round. Is it a circle?"

That is a good and very natural question! A circle is all points *in a plane* that are the same distance from a center point. A sphere is all points *in space* that are the same distance from a center point. A circle is a plane or two-dimensional shape while a sphere is a three-dimensional shape.

But how do you answer the child's question? You might explain that a circle is flat and does not take up space. A sphere is not flat and takes up space. Things shaped like balls—basketballs or baseballs—have a special math name. They are called *spheres*, and we will work with them in the next chapter.

PODCASTING
Professional Development Video Podcasts

Daily Routines
Common Core
SPIRAL REVIEW

Math Board

Problem of the Day
eTransparency 9.2

Calendar Math Say the name of this month. Say the name of last month. Say the name of next month.

 CALENDAR Help a child find the date on the classroom calendar and lead the class in saying it. Point to the numbers on the calendar and have children read them with you. Review the name of this month, last month, and next month.

Vocabulary Builder
Curve

Have children move a hand to trace a straight path in the air.

- **Now trace a curve—a path that is not straight.**

Choose various children to walk to the door in straight paths and in curved paths.

Write some letters such as *o, k, d, w,* and *s* on the board. Let children identify them as having straight or curved parts or both. K and w have straight parts; s and o are curved; d has both straight and curved parts.

Sketch a circle. Have children draw a circle on their MathBoards. Let volunteers describe their circles. Ask children to draw another circle. Then have volunteers tell how their circles are the same and different.

Differentiated Instruction Activities

ELL Language Support
 Verbal / Linguistic
Small Group

Strategy: Model Language

Children can learn correct pronunciation and sentence structure by repeating words and sentences that are modeled by a native speaker.

- When you describe a circle, have children repeat this sentence: **A circle is flat and round and curved.**

- Have children draw a circle. Have them trace it with their finger while saying *round*. Have them point to a curve while saying *curve*.

Repeat the activity if time permits.

See **ELL** Activity Guide for leveled activities.

Enrich
Visual
Individual / Partners

Materials two-dimensional shapes, paper bags, Spinners (blank and 2-section) (see *eTeacher Resources*)

Label the spinner *Circles* on one section and *Not Circles* on the other. Distribute bags filled with shapes. Have children spin the pointer and read what to look for. Have the child pull a shape from the bag that matches what is on the spinner.

- **How did you decide what shape to choose?** I felt it to see if it was round and curved.

- Continue until all shapes are matched. Then have players sort the shapes into two sets: *circles* and *not circles*.

- Ask children to discuss how the two sets are different.

RtI Response to Intervention

Reteach Tier 1
Visual / Kinesthetic
Whole Class / Small Group

Materials large paper circle, paper cup, watch with round face

Display a large paper circle. Help children describe the circle as being round and curved.

- Hold up a paper cup and a round watch face. **Which parts of the paper cup are shaped like a circle?** the bottom and top

- **Which part of the watch is like a circle?** the face

Have children identify and describe items in the classroom with circular surfaces. Then have them draw two things with a circle shape.

Tier 2
Visual / Kinesthetic
Small Group

Draw a square and a circle on the board. Ask children to point to the circle.

- **How do you know which one is the circle?** It is round and curved.

Repeat, asking children to identify a circle by showing a circle and a triangle.

1 ENGAGE

Use six circles to draw a caterpillar on the board.

- **What shape do you see repeated in my caterpillar?** a circle
- **How many circles do you see?** 6

Invite children to draw their own caterpillars using six or more circles.

2 TEACH and TALK

▶ **Listen and Draw** MATHEMATICAL PRACTICES

Read aloud this problem as children listen.

Julia drew a shape and wanted her friend Tara to guess what shape she drew. She gave Tara this hint: "My shape is round and curved. I traced around a cup to draw it." What shape did Julia draw?

Call attention to the circle on the page.

- **Find the worm sitting on the curve and read the word *curve*. Trace your finger around the curve of the circle.**

Have children talk about the curve.

- **Is the curve straight?** no
- **Trace around the curve.**

Reread the problem.

- **What shape did Julia draw?** a circle
- **How do you know?** A circle is round and curved and Julia's hint was that her shape is round and curved.

COMMON CORE — CC.K.G.4 Analyze and compare two- and three-dimensional shapes, in different sizes and orientations, using informal language to describe their similarities, differences, parts (e.g., number of sides each and vertices/"corners") and other attributes (e.g., having sides of equal length).

Name _____

Describe Circles   Lesson **9.2**

Essential Question How can you describe circles?

COMMON CORE STANDARD CC.K.G.4
Analyze, compare, create, and compose shapes.

Listen and Draw REAL WORLD

curve

DIRECTIONS Use your finger to trace around the circle. Talk about the curve. Trace around the curve.

Check children's work.

Chapter 9 • Lesson 2   three hundred sixty-one **361**

© Houghton Mifflin Harcourt Publishing Company

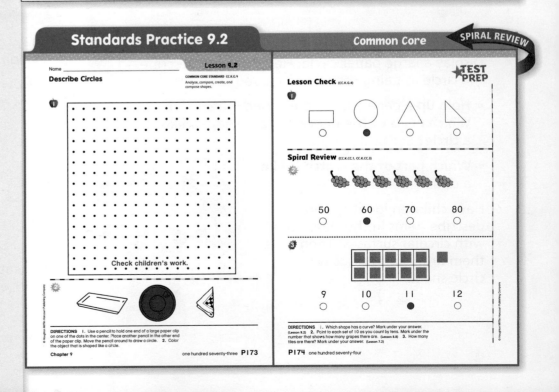

Standards Practice 9.2   **Common Core**   SPIRAL REVIEW

Name _____   Lesson **9.2**
Describe Circles

COMMON CORE STANDARD CC.K.G.4
Analyze, compare, create, and compose shapes.

Check children's work.

DIRECTIONS 1. Use a pencil to hold one end of a large paper clip on one of the dots in the center. Place another pencil in the other end of the paper clip. Move the pencil around to a circle. 2. Color the object that is shaped like a circle.

Chapter 9   one hundred seventy-three **P173**

Lesson Check (CC.K.G.4)   TEST PREP

Spiral Review (CC.K.CC.1, CC.K.CC.3)

50   60   70   80

9   10   11   12

DIRECTIONS 1. Which shape has a curve? Mark under your answer. (Lesson 9.2) 2. Point to each set of 10 as you count by tens. Mark under the number that shows how many grapes there are. (Lesson 8.8) 3. How many tiles are there? Mark under your answer. (Lesson 7.2)

P174 one hundred seventy-four

Share and Show

① 🍎

circle

Check children's work.

② ✓

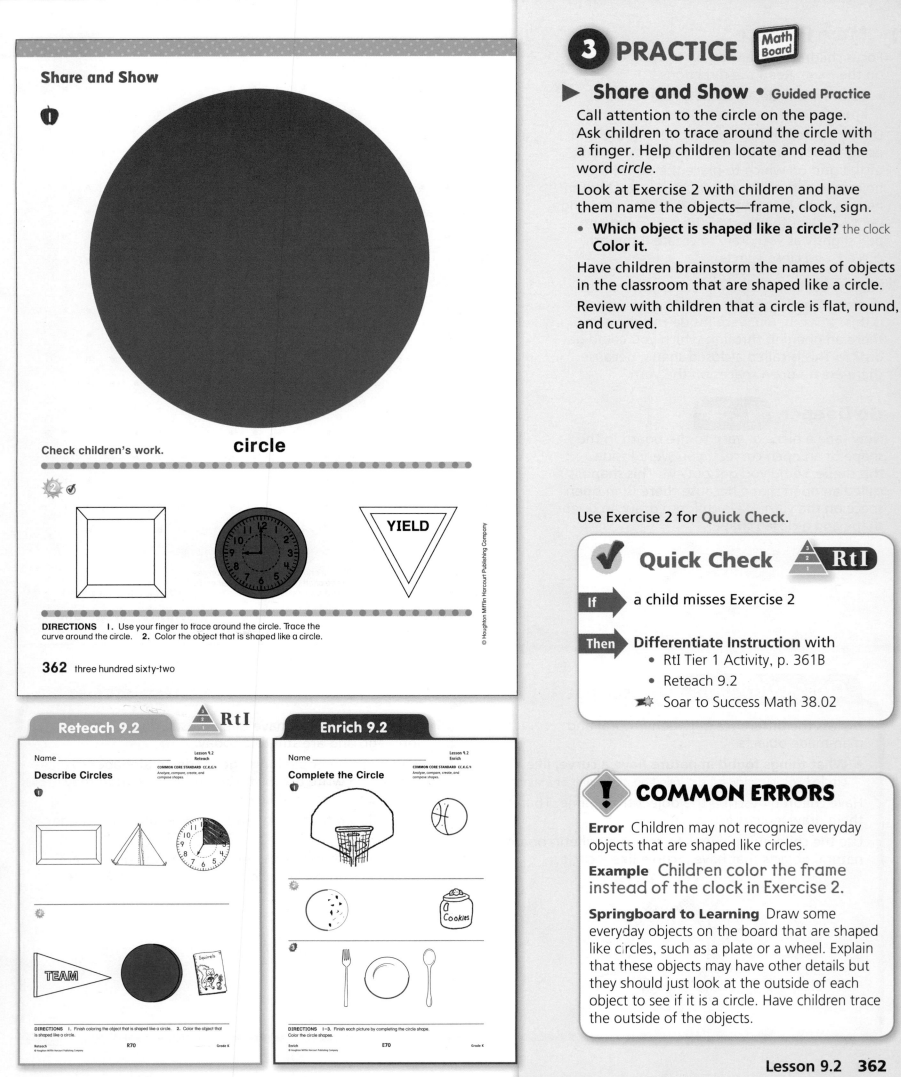

YIELD

© Houghton Mifflin Harcourt Publishing Company

DIRECTIONS 1. Use your finger to trace around the circle. Trace the curve around the circle. **2.** Color the object that is shaped like a circle.

362 three hundred sixty-two

Reteach 9.2 ▲RtI

Name _____

Lesson 9.2
Reteach

Describe Circles

COMMON CORE STANDARD CC.K.G.4
Analyze, compare, create, and compose shapes.

①

✿

TEAM

Squirrels

DIRECTIONS 1. Finish coloring the object that is shaped like a circle. **2.** Color the object that is shaped like a circle.

Reteach
© Houghton Mifflin Harcourt Publishing Company

R70

Grade K

Enrich 9.2

Name _____

Lesson 9.2
Enrich

Complete the Circle

COMMON CORE STANDARD CC.K.G.4
Analyze, compare, create, and compose shapes.

①

✿

Cookies

③

DIRECTIONS 1–3. Finish each picture by completing the circle shape. Color the circle shapes.

Enrich
© Houghton Mifflin Harcourt Publishing Company

E70

Grade K

---

③ PRACTICE 🔲Math Board

▶ Share and Show • Guided Practice

Call attention to the circle on the page. Ask children to trace around the circle with a finger. Help children locate and read the word *circle*.

Look at Exercise 2 with children and have them name the objects—frame, clock, sign.

• **Which object is shaped like a circle?** the clock **Color it.**

Have children brainstorm the names of objects in the classroom that are shaped like a circle.

Review with children that a circle is flat, round, and curved.

Use Exercise 2 for **Quick Check.**

> ✔ **Quick Check** ▲RtI
>
> **If** ▶ a child misses Exercise 2
>
> **Then** ▶ **Differentiate Instruction** with
> • RtI Tier 1 Activity, p. 361B
> • Reteach 9.2
> ⭐ Soar to Success Math 38.02

⚠ COMMON ERRORS

Error Children may not recognize everyday objects that are shaped like circles.

Example Children color the frame instead of the clock in Exercise 2.

Springboard to Learning Draw some everyday objects on the board that are shaped like circles, such as a plate or a wheel. Explain that these objects may have other details but they should just look at the outside of each object to see if it is a circle. Have children trace the outside of the objects.

Lesson 9.2 362

▶ More Practice

Focus children's attention on the dotted grid on the page. Read the directions.

- **To draw a circle, what do you need to know?** A circle is round and curved.

Demonstrate how to draw a circle on the grid using a paper clip. Choose a dot in the middle of the grid on which to place the pencil that holds one end of the paper clip. Show children how to keep that pencil still. Place the drawing pencil in the other end of the paper clip and pull slightly as you draw to create a smooth, curved, and closed circle.

H.O.T. Problem Tape a piece of yarn to the board in the shape of a circle. What shape is this? a circle If you were inside the circle, is there an opening through which you could get out? no This is called a closed shape, because there are no open spaces on the yarn.

Go Deeper `MATHEMATICAL PRACTICES`

Now tape a piece of yarn to the board in the shape of an open curve. If you were inside this shape, could you get out? yes This shape is called an open shape because there is an open space on the yarn. Have children draw an open shape and a closed shape.

Name _____

3️⃣

© Houghton Mifflin Harcourt Publishing Company

DIRECTIONS 3. Use a pencil to hold one end of a large paper clip on one of the dots in the center of the page. Place another pencil in the other end of the paper clip. Move the pencil around to draw a circle.

Check children's work.

Chapter 9 · Lesson 2   three hundred sixty-three **363**

Cross-Curricular   SCIENCE

Discuss the difference between natural and man-made objects.

- **What things found in nature have a curve, like a circle?** Possible answers: sun, raindrop, the center of a sunflower

Have children describe the object they name. Then have them draw a picture.

Use the children's pictures to create a bulletin board of natural objects that have a curve like a circle.

SOCIAL STUDIES

- Discuss how stories have been passed down from long ago and are still told today.
- Explain that people long ago made an alphabet so they could write down stories and information they wanted to share and keep.
- Tell children that some letters and numbers are made with circles.
- Help children name the letters and numbers that are formed using circles: a, b, d, g, o, p, q and 0, 6, 9, 10.

PROBLEM SOLVING

Check children's work.

DIRECTIONS I have a curve. What shape am I? Draw the shape. Tell a friend the name of the shape.

 HOME ACTIVITY • Have your child describe a circle.

364 three hundred sixty-four

© Houghton Mifflin Harcourt Publishing Company

FOR MORE PRACTICE:
Standards Practice Book, pp. P173–P174

▶ **Problem Solving** MATHEMATICAL PRACTICES

Read the riddle for the children. Ask children to explain how they will solve the problem.

- **What shape do you know that has a curve?** a circle
- **What shape will you draw?** a circle

Invite children to share and compare their circles with a friend.

- **What is the same about the circles that you drew?** They are all round, or curved.

4 SUMMARIZE MATHEMATICAL PRACTICES

Essential Question

How can you describe circles? A circle is a flat shape that is round and curved.

Differentiated Instruction   INDEPENDENT ACTIVITIES

Grab-and-Go!
Differentiated Centers Kit

Literature
And the Wheels Go Round
Children read the book and learn about the different shapes used to make a cart.

Games
Follow the Figures
Children identify shapes to follow the game path to the end.

Digital Path

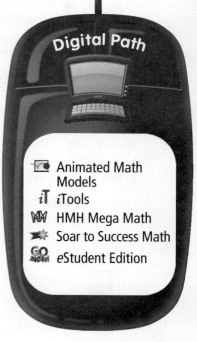

- Animated Math Models
- iT iTools
- MM HMH Mega Math
- Soar to Success Math
- eStudent Edition

Lesson 9.2   364

Identify and Name Squares

LESSON AT A GLANCE

Common Core Standard
Identify and describe shapes (squares, circles, triangles, rectangles, hexagons, cubes, cones, cylinders, and spheres).
CC.K.G.2 Correctly name shapes regardless of their orientations or overall size.

Also CC.K.G.3

Materials
MathBoard,
two-dimensional shapes

Essential Question
How can you identify and name squares?

Lesson Objective
Identify and name two-dimensional shapes including squares.

Vocabulary square, sides, vertex, vertices, corners

Digital Path

iT *iTools*: **Geometry**

MM **HMH Mega Math**

GO **eStudent Edition**

COMMON CORE
PROFESSIONAL DEVELOPMENT

About the Math

Why Teach This?

As children learn more about two-dimensional shapes and their attributes, they are building background for a later, more formal study of geometry. But work with shapes in kindergarten is much more than this. Knowing about shapes lays a foundation for understanding the world and describing both natural objects and those made by humans. Working with shapes strengthens children's spatial sense.

Geometry, with its focus on shapes and positions, is a different aspect of mathematics than working with numbers. But geometry also connects to numbers as children use numbers to tell how many sides or vertices two-dimensional shapes have or how many shapes they are working with. Geometry also connects to other subject areas such as art, science, and social studies.

Shapes can be two-dimensional (lying in a plane, or "flat") or three-dimensional (solid). It is important to introduce correct mathematical language when studying shapes.

 Professional Development Video Podcasts

Daily Routines
Common Core

SPIRAL REVIEW

Problem of the Day
eTransparency **9.3**

Calendar Math Find the date and read it. Tell the name of the month.

CALENDAR Use the class calendar to help a child locate the date and lead the class in reading it, including the month. If the dates on your calendar are square, point out this shape to children.

Fluency Builder

Counting Tape

 EVERY DAY COUNTS®

Materials Counting Tape

Be sure to repeat the same sequence of colors used for each decade before Day 100 when putting up numbers for Day 101 and beyond. On the day that you do reach Day 100, have children discuss what number will come after 100.

- **How many different colors are on the Counting Tape?** 10
- **How many sets of ten colors do you have today?** 10
- **Today you have been in school 100 days.**
- **How many sets of ten are there? How many extra ones?** 10, 0
- **How many groups of ten and how many extra ones will there be tomorrow?** 10, 1

Differentiated Instruction Activities

ELL Language Support
Kinesthetic
Small Group

Strategy: Define

Materials classroom objects

Children can define words by matching visuals to their definitions.

- Show children a variety of classroom objects.
- Have children choose the objects that are square.
- Use the word *square* in context to help children understand the shape.

Repeat the activity with drawings or pictures of various shapes if time permits.

See **ELL** Activity Guide for leveled activities.

Enrich
Visual / Kinesthetic
Individual / Partners

Materials paper squares folded in fourths lengthwise and crosswise, scissors

Have children cut their paper squares along the fold lines, and then exchange them with another child.

- Invite children to rearrange the squares to form the original square.
- Have children write how many squares there are in all. 5

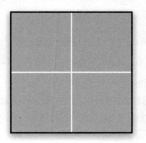

 **RtI** Response to Intervention

Reteach Tier 1
Visual / Kinesthetic
Whole Class / Small Group

Materials large paper cutouts of triangles, circles, and squares

Tape a square or other shape to each child's back.

- Have children take turns tracing the shape with their fingers on the back of another child so that he or she can guess what the shape is. Child guesses *"square"* or *"not a square."*

Tier 2
Visual / Kinesthetic
Small Group

Materials masking tape

Ahead of time, use masking tape to make outlines of squares, rectangles, and triangles on the floor. Make the outlines big enough for a child to stand in.

- Ask a volunteer to stand in a shape that is a square.
- Ask another volunteer to stand in a shape that is NOT a square.

Repeat until every child has had a chance to participate.

LESSON 9.3

1 ENGAGE
 *GO* Online *iTools*

Materials *iTools*: Geometry

Access Prior Knowledge Use *iTools* to show a circle.

- **How would you describe this shape?** It is round and curved.
- **What is the name of this shape?** a circle

Show the name of the shape to children. Have them repeat the word *circle* with you.

- **Trace a circle in the air.**

2 TEACH and TALK
GO Online — HMH Mega Math

► Listen and Draw (MATHEMATICAL PRACTICES)

Materials two-dimensional shapes

Read aloud this problem as children listen.

> *Cheng has a collection of shapes. He wants to sort out all of the squares. How will Cheng know which shapes are squares?*

Help children locate and read the word *squares*.

Hold up a square and identify a side and then point to and count each of the four sides.

- **Squares have four straight sides that match. Trace each side of the square with your finger and count 1, 2, 3, 4.**

Hold up a square. Point to a corner and explain that a corner is where two sides meet. Tell children that another word for corner is *vertex* or *vertices* when you are talking about more than one.

Give children assorted plane shapes. Read the labels on the sorting mat. Then have children sort the shapes.

- **Trace and color the shapes.**
- **How many shapes on the left of the sorting mat are squares?** all the shapes
- **How many shapes on the right of the sorting mat are squares?** none of the shapes
- **How can you describe a square?** It has four straight sides that match and four corners or vertices.

Reread the problem.

- **How will Cheng know which shapes are squares?** He can find the shapes that have four straight sides that match and four corners or vertices.

During discussions in geometry lessons, encourage children to describe shapes in detail. Children may use mathematical terms, such as *vertices*, or informal language, such as *corners*. Either usage is acceptable as long as children accurately describe shapes.

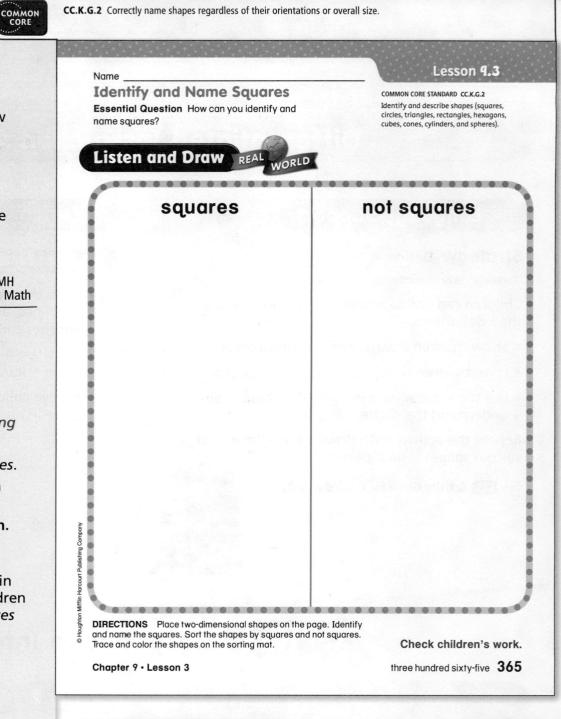

CC.K.G.2 Correctly name shapes regardless of their orientations or overall size.

Lesson 9.3

Name _____

Identify and Name Squares

Essential Question How can you identify and name squares?

COMMON CORE STANDARD CC.K.G.2
Identify and describe shapes (squares, circles, triangles, rectangles, hexagons, cubes, cones, cylinders, and spheres).

Listen and Draw REAL WORLD

squares	not squares

DIRECTIONS Place two-dimensional shapes on the page. Identify and name the squares. Sort the shapes by squares and not squares. Trace and color the shapes on the sorting mat.

Chapter 9 · Lesson 3

Check children's work.

three hundred sixty-five **365**

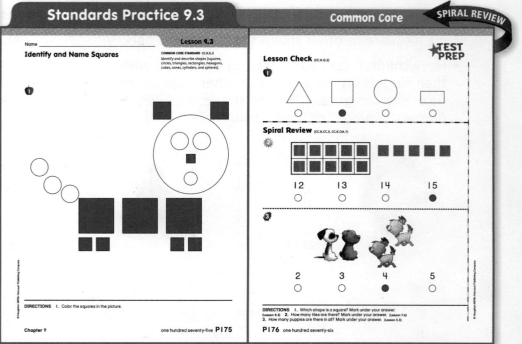

Standards Practice 9.3

Common Core — SPIRAL REVIEW

Name _____

Identify and Name Squares
Lesson 9.3

COMMON CORE STANDARD CC.K.G.2
Identify and describe shapes (squares, circles, triangles, rectangles, hexagons, cubes, cones, cylinders, and spheres).

DIRECTIONS 1. Color the squares in the picture.

Chapter 9

one hundred seventy-five **P175**

Lesson Check (CC.K.G.2)

Spiral Review (CC.K.CC.3, CC.K.OA.1)

12	13	14	15
○	○	○	●

2	3	4	5
○	○	●	○

DIRECTIONS 1. Which shape is a square? Mark under your answer. (Lesson 9.3) 2. How many tiles are there? Mark under your answer. (Lesson 7.6) 3. How many puppies are there in all? Mark under your answer. (Lesson 5.3)

P176 one hundred seventy-six

Share and Show

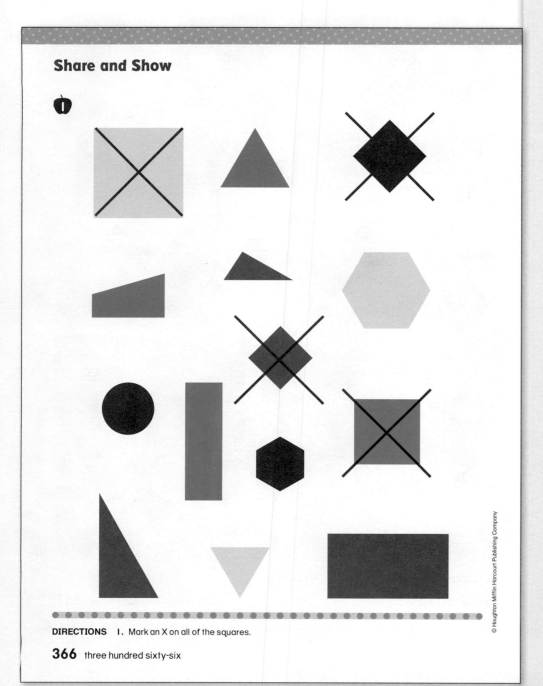

①

© Houghton Mifflin Harcourt Publishing Company

---

③ PRACTICE 〔Math Board〕

▶ **Share and Show** • **Guided Practice**

Call attention to the shapes on the page.

- **Look at the shapes on the page. Are all the shapes the same?** no
- **Are any of the shapes squares?** yes
- **How do you know which ones are squares?**
  A square has four straight sides that match.

Have children find the squares and then mark an X on all the squares on the page. Explain that a square may be turned or be any size. But it is a square if it has four straight sides that match and four vertices.

- **How many squares did you find?** 4
- **What colors are the squares?** yellow, red, blue, and green
- **What do you notice about the blue and red squares?** Possible answer: They are turned a different way than the green and yellow squares.

Discuss with children that when a shape is turned or rotated, it is still the same shape because it still can be described by the number of sides and vertices.

⚠ COMMON ERRORS

Error Children may have difficulty distinguishing squares from other rectangles.

Example Children name other rectangles as squares.

Springboard to Learning Have children trace two touching sides of a square. Then have them trace over two touching sides of a rectangle that is not a square. Ask if the sides match for the square and then for the other rectangle. Explain that a square has four sides that match. If one or more sides are longer, it is not a square.

Lesson 9.3 **366**

► More Practice

Talk about the picture shown on the page.

Ask children to find the shapes in the picture that are squares and then color them. Children might need to be reminded that squares have four straight sides that match and four vertices, or corners.

- **Which parts of the person are made with squares?** legs and arms

Use Exercise 2 for **Quick Check**.

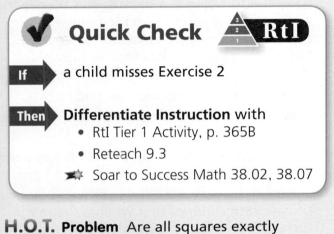

Quick Check

If	a child misses Exercise 2
Then	**Differentiate Instruction** with

- RtI Tier 1 Activity, p. 365B
- Reteach 9.3
- Soar to Success Math 38.02, 38.07

H.O.T. Problem Are all squares exactly the same? No, squares can be different sizes.

Go Deeper
MATHEMATICAL PRACTICES

Children should realize that squares have four sides that match and four vertices, but squares can be any size.

© Houghton Mifflin Harcourt Publishing Company

DIRECTIONS **2.** Color the squares in the picture.

Chapter 9 • Lesson 3

three hundred sixty-seven **367**

COMMON CORE
PROFESSIONAL DEVELOPMENT

Math Talk in Action

John:	I have another shape that has four sides.
Teacher:	Yes. That shape has four sides, too. But it is not a square.
John:	Why?
Teacher:	Because the sides do not match. For a shape to be a square, it has to have four sides that match.
John:	What is the name of this shape?
Teacher:	That is a rectangle. It has four sides, but the four sides do not all match. Squares are also rectangles. But they are special rectangles.
John:	I see two short sides and two long sides.
Teacher:	Yes, and we will talk more about these other rectangles soon.

Amanda:	Are all squares the same?
Teacher:	That is a good question. No, they are not.
Amanda:	Oh, right. They can be different colors.
Teacher:	Yes. They can be different colors, but they can also be different sizes.
Amanda:	I thought all squares had to have sides that match.
Teacher:	Yes. You are correct. A square has four sides that match, but each square can be different. There can be a square with all short sides or one with all long sides.
Amanda:	I get it now.

PROBLEM SOLVING

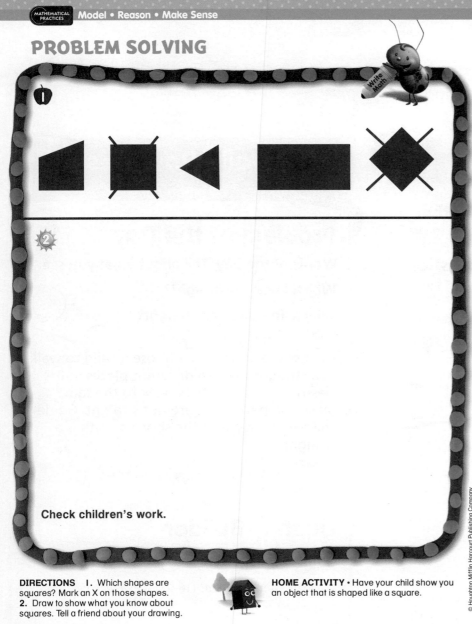

1

2

Check children's work.

DIRECTIONS 1. Which shapes are squares? Mark an X on those shapes. 2. Draw to show what you know about squares. Tell a friend about your drawing.

HOME ACTIVITY • Have your child show you an object that is shaped like a square.

368 three hundred sixty-eight

FOR MORE PRACTICE:
Standards Practice Book, pp. P175–P176

© Houghton Mifflin Harcourt Publishing Company

▶ Problem Solving (MATHEMATICAL PRACTICES)

Have children look at Exercise 1. Ask children to explain how they will solve the problem.

- **How many shapes do you see?** 5
- **Are they all squares?** no
- **How many squares are there?** 2 **Mark an X on the squares.**

Before children draw to show what they know about a square for Exercise 2, ask them to tell what they know. Guide children to describe a square as a shape that has four straight sides that match and four vertices.

After children draw, have them tell a friend about their completed drawings.

 When children have completed this page they may wish to place it in a Math Journal.

4 SUMMARIZE (MATHEMATICAL PRACTICES)

Essential Question

How can you identify and name squares?
I know that a square is a shape with four vertices and four straight sides that match.

Differentiated Instruction · INDEPENDENT ACTIVITIES

Grab-and-Go!™
Differentiated Centers Kit

Literature
And the Wheels Go Round
Children read the book and learn about the different shapes used to make a cart.

Games
Follow the Figures
Children identify shapes to follow the game path to the end.

Digital Path

- Animated Math Models
- iT iTools
- MM HMH Mega Math
- Soar to Success Math
- GO MATH! eStudent Edition

Describe Squares

LESSON AT A GLANCE

Common Core Standard
Analyze, compare, create, and compose shapes.
CC.K.G.4 Analyze and compare two- and three-dimensional shapes, in different sizes and orientations, using informal language to describe their similarities, differences, parts (e.g., number of sides and vertices/"corners") and other attributes (e.g., having sides of equal length).

Also CC.K.G.2, CC.K.G.5

Lesson Objective
Describe attributes of squares.

Essential Question
How can you describe squares?

Vocabulary **sides of equal length**

Materials
MathBoard, two-color counters

Digital Path

iT *iTools*: Geometry

MM HMH Mega Math

GO eStudent Edition

COMMON CORE PROFESSIONAL DEVELOPMENT

About the Math

Teaching for Depth

In this lesson, children do activities with squares. The activities engage children in using their hands and minds and helps them internalize the content.

As children explore two-dimensional shapes, help them develop a strong understanding of the similarities and differences by pointing out attributes of straight sides, vertices, and curves. It is important to use correct mathematical language when describing attributes. In the lessons about squares and rectangles emphasize that the corners or vertices are square corners and square vertices. This will prevent misunderstanding when children learn about parallelograms in later grades.

Professional Development Video Podcasts

Daily Routines
Common Core

SPIRAL REVIEW

Math Board

Problem of the Day
eTransparency 9.4

Words of the Day Tell about what you see.

Which lines are *straight*?

Which lines are *not straight*?
Check children's answers.

Discuss the questions. Choose a child to walk in a straight path to different places in the classroom. Have others walk to the same places on paths that are not straight. Guide children to see that the shortest path is a straight one.

Fluency Builder

Count to 20

Materials Numeral Cards (16–23) (see *eTeacher Resources*)

Draw one row of 10 and a second row of 9 oranges on the board.

- **How would you start counting the oranges?** Start from the beginning of the row.

Lead children in counting.

- **How many oranges are there?** 19

Show the numeral card for 19 and have children read it.

- **What number comes after 19?** 20

Draw one more orange at the end of the row of 9. Show the numeral card for 20 and have children read it.

Draw a line to divide the row in half so that each set has 10. Lead children in counting the first set from 1 to 10. Write **10** above the set. Do the same for the second set.

- **How many is 10 ones and 10 more ones?** 20

Differentiated Instruction Activities

ELL Language Support
🕐 Visual / Linguistic
Small Group

Strategy: Model Language

Children can learn correct pronunciation and sentence structure by repeating words and sentences that are modeled by a native speaker.

- Have children repeat each of the following sentences:
A square has four sides of equal length. A square has four square vertices.

- **How are the number of sides and number of vertices the same?**
There are four sides and four vertices.

- Have children draw a square and label the number of sides and vertices.

See **ELL** Activity Guide for leveled activities.

Enrich
🕐 Kinesthetic
Individual / Partners

Materials: Pattern Blocks, crayons, paper

Invite children to use blocks to build squares of different sizes.

- Have children trace the different squares that they created to show their work.

- Have children exchange their drawings with a partner and count and write the number of sides and vertices of the large square.

- Ask children to discuss whether using different numbers of blocks to build a square changes the number of sides and vertices the square has.

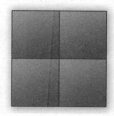

▲ RtI Response to Intervention

Reteach Tier 1
🕐 Visual / Kinesthetic
Whole Class / Small Group

Draw a square and a circle on the board. Ask children to point to the square.

- **How do you know which one is the square?** It has four sides of equal length. It has four square vertices.

- Draw a square and another rectangle on the board. **How many square vertices does each shape have?** 4 **What is different about these shapes?** The lengths of the sides in one shape are not equal in length. **Which one is a square?** The shape that has four sides of equal length and four square vertices.

Repeat, asking children to identify a square by showing a square and a triangle.

Tier 2
🕐 Visual / Kinesthetic
Small Group

Materials Pattern Blocks

Show children the orange square block and the green triangle block.

- **Which shape is a square?** the orange shape

- **How do you know?** It has four sides of equal length. It has four square vertices.

Repeat several times with different blocks.

1 ENGAGE

Materials clay, toothpicks

Access Prior Knowledge Have children make models of squares using clay and toothpicks.

- **Roll the clay into four small balls for the corners. Press the ends of four toothpicks into the clay to form a square. Make sure the shape lies flat and is closed.**

- **What shape do you have?** a square

- **How do you know it is a square?** It has four straight sides that match and 4 square vertices.

2 TEACH and TALK

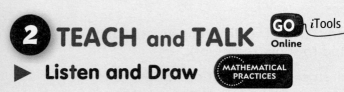

▶ **Listen and Draw** MATHEMATICAL PRACTICES

Read aloud this problem as children listen.

Alanna needs a square-shaped frame for her soccer picture. How many sides should the frame have?

Call attention to the square on the page.

- **Trace a finger around the square. Find the worm sitting on the side and the word *side*.**

- **The length of a side tells how far from one end to the other end. If sides are of equal length, it means that they have the same length.**

- **How many sides of equal length does the square have?** 4

- **Trace around the sides.**

Point to a corner and explain that a square corner is where two sides meet like the corner of a piece of notebook paper. Explain that another word for corner is *vertex*. Explain that when children talk about more than one vertex in a shape, they use the word *vertices*.

- **Find the worm sitting on the vertex and the word *vertex*.**

- **How many square vertices, or square corners, does the square have?** 4

- **Draw an arrow pointing to another vertex.**

- **How can you describe the sides of a square?** A square has four sides that are all the same length.

Reread the problem.

- **How many sides of equal length should Alanna's frame have?** 4

CC.K.G.4 Analyze and compare two- and three-dimensional shapes, in different sizes and orientations, using informal language to describe their similarities, differences, parts (e.g., number of sides and vertices/"corners") and other attributes (e.g., having sides of equal length).

Name _____

Describe Squares

Essential Question How can you describe squares?

Lesson 9.4

COMMON CORE STANDARD CC.K.G.4
Analyze, compare, create, and compose shapes.

Listen and Draw

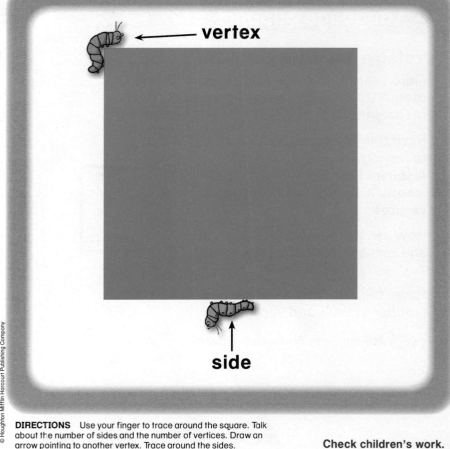

DIRECTIONS Use your finger to trace around the square. Talk about the number of sides and the number of vertices. Draw an arrow pointing to another vertex. Trace around the sides.

Chapter 9 • Lesson 4

Check children's work.

three hundred sixty-nine **369**

Standards Practice 9.4 Common Core SPIRAL REVIEW

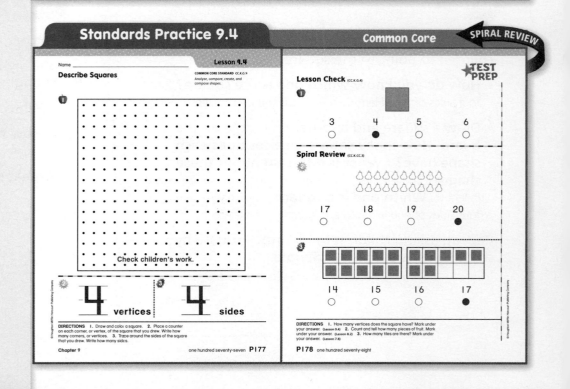

Share and Show

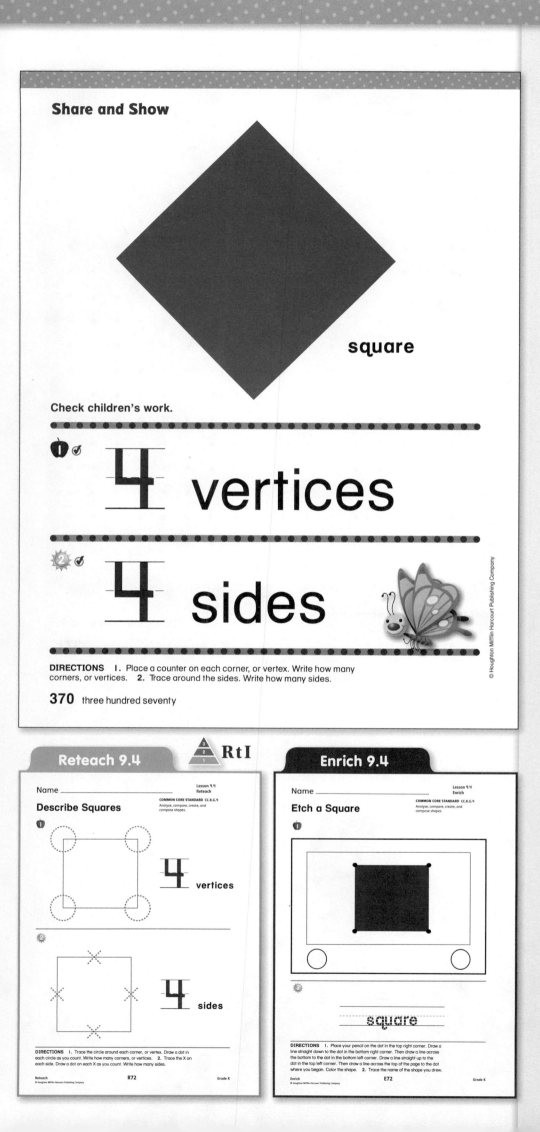

square

Check children's work.

1 ✓

4 vertices

2 ✓

4 sides

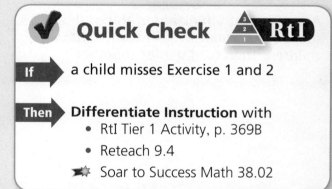

DIRECTIONS 1. Place a counter on each corner, or vertex. Write how many corners, or vertices. 2. Trace around the sides. Write how many sides.

© Houghton Mifflin Harcourt Publishing Company

Reteach 9.4 ▲RtI

Name _____

Describe Squares

Lesson 9.4
Reteach

COMMON CORE STANDARD CC.K.G.4
Analyze, compare, create, and compose shapes.

1

4 vertices

4 sides

DIRECTIONS 1. Trace the circle around each corner, or vertex. Draw a dot in each circle as you count. Write how many corners, or vertices. 2. Trace the X on each side. Draw a dot on each X as you count. Write how many sides.

Reteach
© Houghton Mifflin Harcourt Publishing Company

R72

Grade K

Enrich 9.4

Name _____

Etch a Square

Lesson 9.4
Enrich

COMMON CORE STANDARD CC.K.G.4
Analyze, compare, create, and compose shapes.

1

square

DIRECTIONS 1. Place your pencil on the dot in the top right corner. Draw a line straight down to the dot in the bottom right corner. Then draw a line across the bottom to the dot in the bottom left corner. Draw a line straight up to the dot in the top left corner. Then draw a line across the top of the page to the dot where you began. Color the shape. 2. Trace the name of the shape you drew.

Enrich
© Houghton Mifflin Harcourt Publishing Company

E72

Grade K

---

③ PRACTICE 📋 Math Board

► Share and Show • Guided Practice

Materials two-color counters

Call attention to the blue square on the page. Remind children that, even though the square has been turned, it is still a square. Ask children to trace around the square with a finger. Have children use counters to complete the activity.

- **Place a counter on each corner, or vertex. How many vertices do you see?** 4 **Write the number.**

Have children remove the counters.

- **Place a counter on each side. What number will you write?** 4 **Why?** because the square has four sides

- **What do you know about the four sides of a square?** They are all of equal length.

Read the completed lines with the children: **4 vertices, 4 sides.** Explain that those words help describe a square.

- **How many sides of equal length and square vertices does this square have?** four sides; four square vertices

Use Exercises 1 and 2 for **Quick Check.**

✓ **Quick Check** ▲RtI

If → a child misses Exercise 1 and 2

Then → **Differentiate Instruction** with
- RtI Tier 1 Activity, p. 369B
- Reteach 9.4
- ⭐ Soar to Success Math 38.02

⚠ COMMON ERRORS

Error Children may not be able to identify the vertices.

Example Children do not know the number of vertices that a square has.

Springboard to Learning Draw a square. Ask children to locate the corners. Remind them that *vertex* means corner, or where the sides meet. Then ask children to draw a dot on each vertex (corner) and then count them.

▶ More Practice

Focus children's attention on the dotted grid on the page. Read the directions.

- **To draw a square, what do you need to know?** A square has four sides of equal length and four square corners, or square vertices.

Demonstrate how to draw a square on the grid using four dots as the four vertices. Trace a dot as your first vertex. Be sure to count aloud the number of spaces between the dots each time you draw a side. This demonstrates that all the sides are of equal length and square corners.

Have children draw a square. Explain that it can be any size but must have sides of equal length.

- **How can you tell if all the sides are the same?** I can count the spaces between the dots on each side.

- **How can you find the vertices?** I can find where the sides meet.

After children complete a square, help them count the spaces between the dots to make sure that the sides of the square are of equal length and the vertices are square. Then have children color their squares.

H.O.T. Problem Make a smaller square than the one you drew.

- **What is the smallest square you can make by connecting dots on the grid?** Check children's work.

Go Deeper [MATHEMATICAL PRACTICES]

Ask children to think about things that are shaped like squares. Brainstorm a list with children. Then read the list together.

Name _____

③

© Houghton Mifflin Harcourt Publishing Company

DIRECTIONS **3.** Draw and color a square.

Chapter 9 • Lesson 4

Check children's work.

PROBLEM SOLVING

Check children's work.

DIRECTIONS I have 4 sides of equal length and 4 vertices. What shape am I? Draw the shape. Tell a friend the name of the shape.

HOME ACTIVITY • Have your child describe a square.

372 three hundred seventy-two

FOR MORE PRACTICE:
Standards Practice Book, pp. P177–P178

© Houghton Mifflin Harcourt Publishing Company

▶ **Problem Solving** (MATHEMATICAL PRACTICES)

Read the riddle for the children. Ask children to explain how they will solve the riddle.

- **What shape has four sides of equal length?** a scuare
- **What shape has four square vertices?** a square; also accept rectangle
- **What shape has both four sides of equal length and four square vertices?** a square
- **What shape will you draw?** a square

Remind children to try to make the sides of equal length and the vertices square as they draw.

Invite children to tell a friend about their drawings. Lead them to compare the number of sides in their squares. Then have them compare the number of vertices in their squares.

4 SUMMARIZE (MATHEMATICAL PRACTICES)

Essential Question

How can you describe squares? A square is a shape that has four sides of equal length and four square vertices.

Differentiated Instruction INDEPENDENT ACTIVITIES

Grab-and-Go!
Differentiated Centers Kit

Literature
And the Wheels Go Round
Children read the book and learn about the different shapes used to make a cart.

Games
Follow the Figures
Children identify shapes to follow the game path to the end.

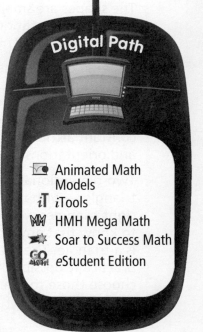

Digital Path

- Animated Math Models
- iT iTools
- MM HMH Mega Math
- Soar to Success Math
- eStudent Edition

Identify and Name Triangles

LESSON AT A GLANCE

Common Core Standard
Identify and describe shapes (squares, circles, triangles, rectangles, hexagons, cubes, cones, cylinders, and spheres).
CC.K.G.2 Correctly name shapes regardless of their orientations or overall size.

Also CC.K.G.3

Materials
MathBoard,
two-dimensional shapes

Lesson Objective
Identify and name two-dimensional shapes including triangles.

Essential Question
How can you identify and name triangles?

Vocabulary **triangle**

Digital Path

iT **iTools: Geometry**

GO MATH **eStudent Edition**

MM **HMH Mega Math**

Daily Routines
Math Board

Common Core

Problem of the Day
eTransparency 9.5

Calendar Math **Find and read the date on the class calendar.**

Tell about yesterday, today, and tomorrow.

CALENDAR Help a child find the date on the class calendar and lead the class in reading it. Point out yesterday, today, and tomorrow; have the class read them.

COMMON CORE MATHEMATICAL PRACTICES

Using Two-Dimensional Shapes

Using two-dimensional shape manipulatives as children learn shape names and attributes helps children make visual discriminations. Working with the shapes keeps children's attention; handling and showing the two-dimensional shapes aids children's explanations as they refer to them.

The shapes are small, and as children move them to different orientations, they begin to understand that shapes such as triangles can appear many different ways.

Children can feel the sides and vertices of the two-dimensional shapes, point to them, and trace along the sides with their fingers. Because they deal with shapes of different sizes and colors, children learn that shapes have constant attributes no matter what their sizes, colors, and orientations.

Two-dimensional shape manipulatives include equilateral triangles—with three equal sides and angles—and right triangles with one right angle. Children also need to know that any closed shape with exactly three sides is a triangle. The shape manipulatives also are as flat as practically possible. For *real world* examples of triangles, choose those that are flat like pieces of paper.

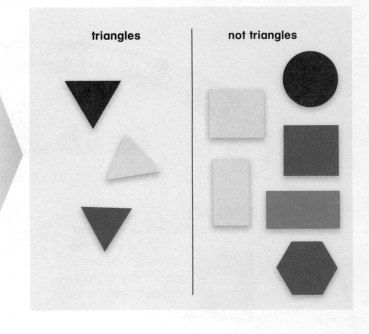

triangles | not triangles

Differentiated Instruction Activities

ELL Language Support

Verbal / Linguistic
Small Group

Strategy: Describe

Materials two-dimensional shapes

Children can practice their comprehension by describing what they have seen or heard.

- Show children several squares and triangles.
- Identify and name each shape together.
- **What is the difference between a square and a triangle?** Make sure that children mention that a square has four straight sides and a triangle has three straight sides.

Repeat the activity if time permits.

See **ELL** Activity Guide for leveled activities.

Enrich
Kinesthetic
Individual / Partners

Materials triangle and square Pattern Blocks, paper bag

Place an assortment of triangle and square pattern blocks in a paper bag. Demonstrate how to reach in, pick a shape, and describe and name the shape before pulling it out.

- Have children take a turn describing and guessing the name of the shape before they pull it out of the bag.
- Continue until all of the shapes in the bag have been described and named.

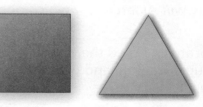

RtI Response to Intervention

Reteach Tier 1
Visual / Kinesthetic
Whole Class / Small Group

Materials long pieces of yarn

Form a triangle, a circle, and a square on the floor with yarn.

- Have children identify the triangle and take turns walking along it.

Repeat until each child has had a turn.

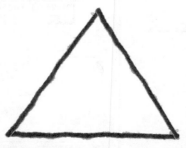

Tier 2
Kinesthetic / Verbal
Small Group

Ask three children to lie down on the floor and form a triangle with their bodies. Ask the other children to make sure the shape the children have formed on the floor is a triangle. **Why is this a triangle?** The shape has three straight sides.

- Ask four children to lie down on the floor and form a shape that is not a triangle with their bodies. Ask the other children to make sure that the shape that the children have formed on the floor is not a triangle. **Why is this not a triangle?** Possible answer: The shape has more than three sides.

Repeat until every child has had a chance to be part of making a shape.

1 ENGAGE

Materials masking tape

Access Prior Knowledge Make a large square on the classroom floor using masking tape.

Invite children to take turns walking on the square. Have children count each side as they walk on it.

Then ask a volunteer to stand inside or outside of the square.

2 TEACH and TALK GO Online iTools

▶ **Listen and Draw** MATHEMATICAL PRACTICES

Materials two-dimensional shapes

Read aloud this problem as children listen.

Aidan has a button collection. He wants to sort all the buttons that are shaped like triangles. How will Aidan know which ones to sort?

Help children locate and read the word *triangles*. Hold up a triangle and trace the sides with your finger.

- **A triangle has three straight sides. The three sides do not have to be the same length. Not all triangles look the same.**

Show different types of triangles, pointing out that they all have three sides.

- **Look at your two-dimensional shapes. Sort them on the mat in sets of *triangles* and *not triangles*. Then trace and color them.**
- **How many shapes on the left of the sorting mat are triangles?** all of the shapes
- **How many shapes on the right of the sorting mat are triangles?** none of the shapes
- **What is the same about all the triangles?** They all have three straight sides.

Reread the problem.

- **How will Aidan know which buttons are shaped like triangles?** He can find the buttons that have three straight sides.

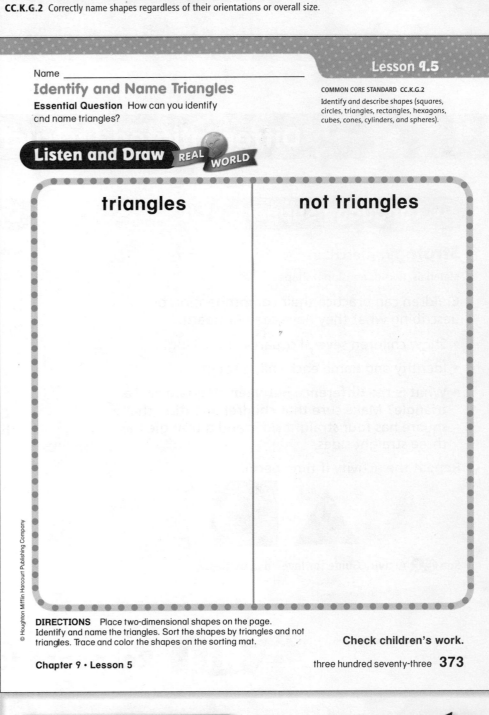

Name _____

Identify and Name Triangles

Essential Question How can you identify and name triangles?

Lesson 9.5

COMMON CORE STANDARD CC.K.G.2
Identify and describe shapes (squares, circles, triangles, rectangles, hexagons, cubes, cones, cylinders, and spheres).

Listen and Draw REAL WORLD

triangles	not triangles

DIRECTIONS Place two-dimensional shapes on the page. Identify and name the triangles. Sort the shapes by triangles and not triangles. Trace and color the shapes on the sorting mat.

Check children's work.

Chapter 9 • Lesson 5

three hundred seventy-three **373**

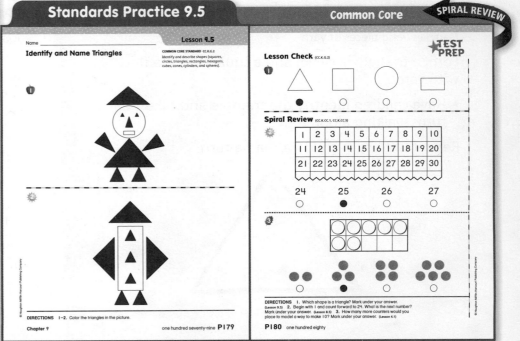

Standards Practice 9.5 **Common Core** SPIRAL REVIEW

Name _____

Identify and Name Triangles

COMMON CORE STANDARD CC.K.G.2
Identify and describe shapes (squares, circles, triangles, rectangles, hexagons, cubes, cones, cylinders, and spheres).

Lesson Check (CC.K.G.2)

Spiral Review (CC.K.CC.1, CC.K.CC.5)

DIRECTIONS 1–2. Color the triangles in the picture.

DIRECTIONS 1. Which shape is a triangle? Mark under your answer. (Lesson 9.5) 2. Begin with 1 and count forward to 24. What is the next number? Mark under your answer. (Lesson 8.5) 3. How many more counters would you place to model a way to make 10? Mark under your answer. (Lesson 4.1)

Chapter 9

one hundred seventy-nine **P179**

P180 one hundred eighty

Share and Show

①

DIRECTIONS 1. Mark an X on all of the triangles.

374 three hundred seventy-four

▶ **Share and Show** • **Guided Practice**

Call attention to the shapes in Exercise 1.

- **Look at the shapes on the page. Are all of the shapes the same?** no
- **Can you name any of the shapes?** Children may name squares, circles, triangles, hexagons, and rectangles.
- **Are any of the shapes triangles?** yes **How do you know?** A triangle has three straight sides.

Have children find all of the triangles on the page and then mark an X on each one.

- **How many triangles did you find?** 5
- **Do you see triangles that look the same but are turned different ways? If so, which ones?** yes, the green and red; also the yellow and blue

Discuss that triangles can be different sizes and be in different positions, but they all have three straight sides.

Reteach 9.5 ▲ RtI

Name _____

Identify and Name Triangles

COMMON CORE STANDARD CC.K.G.2
Identify and describe shapes (squares, circles, triangles, rectangles, hexagons, cubes, cones, cylinders, and spheres).

①

DIRECTIONS 1. Place a triangle on each shaded triangle. Color the other triangles in the picture.

Reteach R73 Grade K
© Houghton Mifflin Harcourt Company

Enrich 9.5

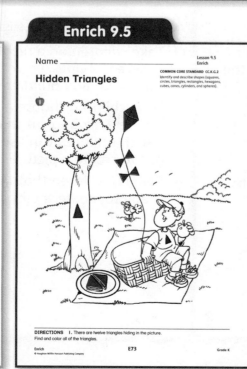

Name _____

Hidden Triangles

COMMON CORE STANDARD CC.K.G.2
Identify and describe shapes (squares, circles, triangles, rectangles, hexagons, cubes, cones, cylinders, and spheres).

①

DIRECTIONS 1. There are twelve triangles hiding in the picture. Find and color all of the triangles.

Enrich E73 Grade K
© Houghton Mifflin Harcourt Publishing Company

⚠ COMMON ERRORS

Error Children may have difficulty identifying triangles.

Example Children name other shapes as triangles.

Springboard to Learning Have children trace a triangle, using a different color for each side. Then have them count the sides and establish that a triangle has three sides. Then have children differentiate a triangle from other shapes the same way.

► More Practice

Talk about the picture in Exercise 2 and explain that the objects pictured are made up of triangles and other shapes. Ask the children to identify the triangles and then color them. If children can, have them identify the other shapes.

Use Exercise 2 for **Quick Check**.

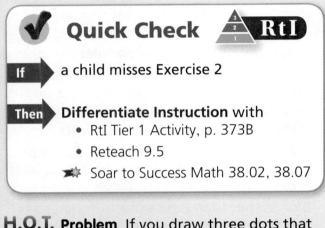

Quick Check RtI

If ➤ a child misses Exercise 2

Then ➤ **Differentiate Instruction** with
- RtI Tier 1 Activity, p. 373B
- Reteach 9.5
- ✭ Soar to Success Math 38.02, 38.07

H.O.T. Problem If you draw three dots that are not in a row, and you connect them, what shape will you make? a triangle

Go Deeper

MATHEMATICAL PRACTICES

Children need an understanding that they will be connecting the dots so that a triangle will be formed. Have them complete the H.O.T. Problem and share their triangles.

Name _____

© Houghton Mifflin Harcourt Publishing Company

DIRECTIONS **2.** Color the triangles in the picture.

Chapter 9 • Lesson 5

three hundred seventy-five **375**

PROBLEM SOLVING

Check children's work.

DIRECTIONS 1. Which shapes are triangles? Mark an X on those shapes. 2. Draw to show what you know about triangles. Tell a friend about your drawing.

HOME ACTIVITY • Have your child show you an object that is shaped like a triangle.

376 three hundred seventy-six

FOR MORE PRACTICE:
Standards Practice Book, pp. P179–P180

© Houghton Mifflin Harcourt Publishing Company

▶ Problem Solving MATHEMATICAL PRACTICES

Have children look at Exercise 1. Read the problem and ask children to explain how they will solve it.

- **How many shapes do you see?** 5
- **Are they all triangles?** no
- **How many circles do you see?** 1
- **How would you describe it?** It is round and curved.
- **How many squares do you see?** 1 **How many straight sides does it have?** 4
- **How many triangles do you see?** 2 **How many straight sides do they each have?** 3

Ask children to mark an X on the triangles.

Before children do Exercise 2, ask them to tell what they know about a triangle. Guide children to describe a triangle as a shape that has three straight sides.

After children draw, have them tell a friend about their drawing.

4 SUMMARIZE MATHEMATICAL PRACTICES

Essential Question

How can you identify and name triangles?
I know that a triangle is a shape with three straight sides.

Differentiated Instruction INDEPENDENT ACTIVITIES

Grab-and-Go!™
Differentiated Centers Kit

Literature
And the Wheels Go Round
Children read the book and learn about the different shapes used to make a cart.

Games
Follow the Figures
Children identify shapes to follow the game path to the end.

Digital Path

- Animated Math Models
- iT iTools
- MM HMH Mega Math
- Soar to Success Math
- eStudent Edition

Describe Triangles

LESSON AT A GLANCE

Common Core Standard
Analyze, compare, create, and compose shapes.
CC.K.G.4 Analyze and compare two- and three-dimensional shapes, in different sizes and orientations, using informal language to describe their similarities, differences, parts (e.g., number of sides and vertices/"corners") and other attributes (e.g., having sides of equal length).

Also CC.K.G.2, CC.K.G.5

Lesson Objective
Describe attributes of triangles.

Essential Question
How can you describe triangles?

Materials
MathBoard, two-color counters

Digital Path

 iTiTools: Geometry

eStudent Edition

MM HMH Mega Math

COMMON CORE
PROFESSIONAL DEVELOPMENT

About the Math

If Children Ask

A child may hold up a paper triangle or two-dimensional shape manipulative and say, "My triangle has two sides—the front side and the back side. Is that right?" The child who asks a question like this clearly is confused about what we mean by sides of shapes. Since we refer to the front side and back side of pieces of paper, it is easy to see how such confusion arises.

Explain that sides of shapes form the outside borders of that shape. Sides of triangles, squares, hexagons, and rectangles are straight. Have the child trace a finger along the side of a paper triangle and the sides of a two-dimensional shape manipulative. Help the child count each side as it is traced.

You might also have the child glue three short pieces of yarn to paper to form a triangle. Saying, "Use three lines of glue. Now lay down the three pieces of yarn for the three sides" may help to clarify. Children may also use dough to make three long thin "snakes," then mold these together as sides of a triangle.

 **Professional Development Video Podcasts**

Daily Routines
Math Board

Common Core
SPIRAL REVIEW

Problem of the Day
eTransparency 9.6

Numbers of the Day

Count as your teacher points to the numbers.

11   12   13   14   15   16   17   18   19

Tell what the number 14 means.

Tell what the number 18 means.
ten ones and four ones; ten ones and eight ones

Lead children in counting from 11 to 19. Point to numerals at random and have children read them. Lead a discussion of what 14 means. 10 ones and 4 ones

Repeat for 18 and other teen numbers.

Fluency Builder
Counting within 50

Materials Fifty Chart (see *eTeacher Resources*)

Show children a fifty chart. Lead them in counting from 1 to 50.

Ask a volunteer to point to the fifty chart as you ask the following questions.

- **What number is one greater than 43?** 44
- **What number is two less than 49?** 47
- Have a different volunteer repeat with similar questions.

Differentiated Instruction Activities

ELL Language Support
 Auditory / Visual
Small Group

Strategy: Rephrase

Children can demonstrate their understanding by rephrasing what they have heard or read.

- Show children a drawing of a large triangle.

- **I can tell that this shape is a triangle. A triangle has three straight sides. A triangle has three vertices.**

- Have children rephrase your description of the triangle.

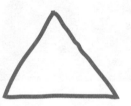

Repeat the activity if time permits.

See **ELL** Activity Guide for leveled activities.

Enrich
Kinesthetic
Individual / Partners

Materials two six-foot pieces of yarn

Have three children hold a loop of yarn to build a triangle. **How many sides and vertices does it have?** 3; 3

- Challenge children to move, but still form a triangle. **Is this still a triangle? How can you tell?** Yes, it still has three sides and three vertices.

- Repeat with three more volunteers. Guide children to rotate and move to change the proportions of the sides of the triangle.

- **How many sides will a triangle always have?** 3

▲ RtI Response to Intervention

Reteach Tier 1
Visual / Kinesthetic
Whole Class / Small Group

Materials nine craft sticks, glue, construction paper, crayons in three colors

Have children work in groups of three. Distribute three craft sticks to each child.

- Have children color their craft sticks so that each craft stick is a different color.

- Ask children to glue craft sticks onto paper to make triangles that each have three different-colored sides.

- **How do you know the shape is a triangle?** It has three sides. It has three vertices.

Tier 2
Kinesthetic / Visual
Small Group

Materials Pattern Blocks

Draw some large triangles on the board. Have children take turns saying *triangle* as they trace over the shape with their fingers.

- Show children the orange square pattern block and the green triangle pattern block. **Which shape is a triangle?** the green shape **How do you know that the green shape is a triangle?** It has three sides. It has three vertices.

- Show children the green triangle pattern block and the red trapezoid pattern block. **Which shape is a triangle?** the green shape **How do you know that the green shape is a triangle?** It has three sides. It has three vertices.

1 ENGAGE

Materials clay, toothpicks

Access Prior Knowledge Have children make models of triangles using clay and toothpicks.

- **Roll the clay into three small balls for the corners. Press the ends of three toothpicks into the clay to form a triangle. Make sure the shape is closed.**
- **What shape do you have?** a triangle
- **How do you know it is a triangle?** It has three straight sides.

2 TEACH and TALK 🔵 iTools Online

▶ **Listen and Draw**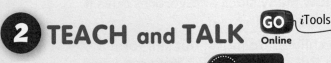

Read aloud this problem as children listen.

Sofia placed three straws on a table and made a shape. The end of each straw touched the end of another straw. What shape did Sofia make?

Call attention to the triangle on the page.

- **Trace a finger around the triangle. Find the worm sitting on the side and the word *side*.**
- **How many sides does the triangle have?** 3
- **Trace around the sides.**
- **Find the worm sitting on the vertex and the word *vertex*. How many vertices does a triangle have?** 3

Remind children that the words *vertices* and *corners* mean the same thing, places where two sides meet.

- **Draw an arrow pointing to a different vertex.** Check visually.
- **Elicit from children that a triangle has three straight sides and three vertices, or corners.**

Reread the problem.

- **What shape did Sofia make with her three straws?** a triangle
- **How do you know?** Sofia used three straws for three sides and made three vertices.

COMMON CORE

CC.K.G.4 Analyze and compare two- and three-dimensional shapes, in different sizes and orientations, using informal language to describe their similarities, differences, parts (e.g., number of sides and vertices/"corners") and other attributes (e.g., having sides of equal length).

Name _____

Lesson 9.6

Describe Triangles

Essential Question How can you describe triangles?

COMMON CORE STANDARD CC.K.G.4
Analyze, compare, create, and compose shapes.

Listen and Draw

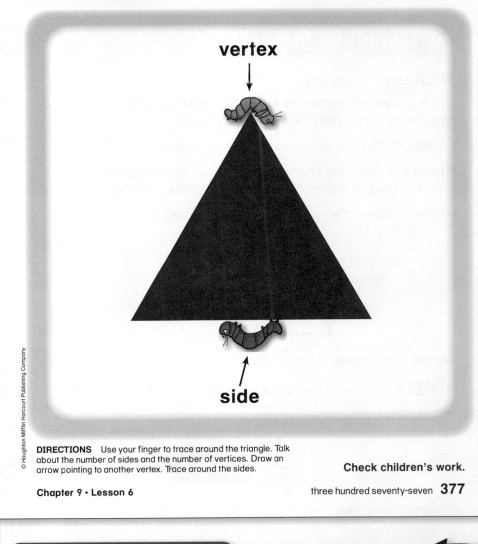

© Houghton Mifflin Harcourt Publishing Company

DIRECTIONS Use your finger to trace around the triangle. Talk about the number of sides and the number of vertices. Draw an arrow pointing to another vertex. Trace around the sides.

Check children's work.

Chapter 9 · Lesson 6

three hundred seventy-seven **377**

Standards Practice 9.6   **Common Core**   SPIRAL REVIEW

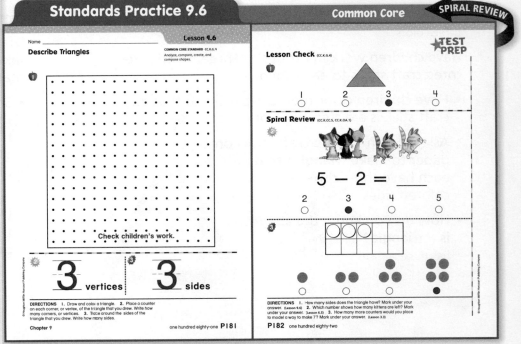

Name _____

Lesson 9.6

Describe Triangles

COMMON CORE STANDARD CC.K.G.4
Analyze, compare, create, and compose shapes.

Lesson Check (CC.K.G.4)

⬆ TEST PREP

① [grid of dots]

Check children's work.

3 vertices   **3** sides

DIRECTIONS 1. Draw and color a triangle. **2.** Place a counter on each corner, or vertex, of the triangle that you drew. Write how many corners, or vertices. **3.** Trace around the sides of the triangle you drew. Write how many sides.

Chapter 9   one hundred eighty-one • P181

① [triangle]
  1   2   3   4
  ○   ○   ●   ○

Spiral Review (CC.K.CC.5, CC.K.OA.1)

$5 - 2 =$ _____

  2   3   4   5
  ○   ●   ○   ○

③ [ten frames with dots]

DIRECTIONS 1. How many sides does the triangle have? Mark under your answer. (Lesson 9.6) **2.** Which number shows how many kittens are left? Mark under your answer. (Lesson 6.5) **3.** How many more counters would you place to model a way to make 7? Mark under your answer. (Lesson 3.5)

P182   one hundred eighty-two

Share and Show

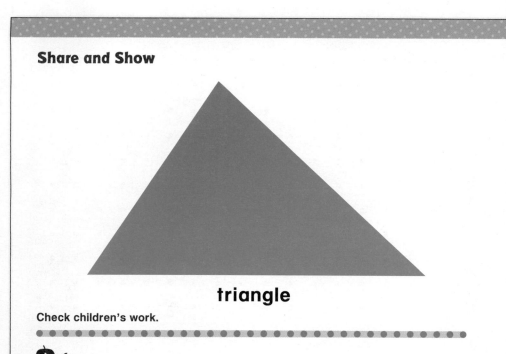

triangle

Check children's work.

❶ ✓

3 vertices

❷ ✓

3 sides

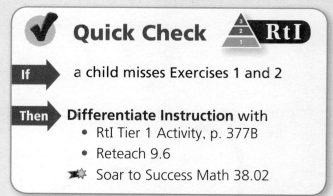

DIRECTIONS 1. Place a counter on each corner, or vertex. Write how many corners, or vertices. 2. Trace around the sides. Write how many sides.

378 three hundred seventy-eight

Reteach 9.6 ▲ RtI

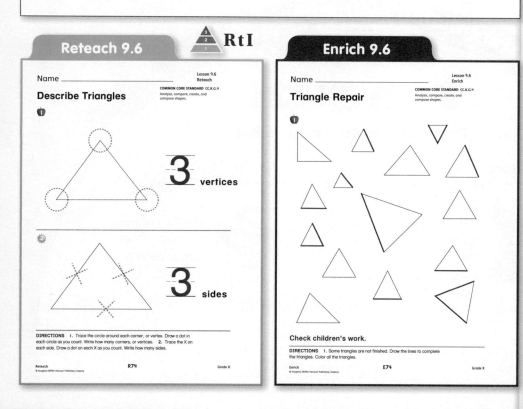

Enrich 9.6

---

③ PRACTICE 📱 Math Board

▶ **Share and Show** • Guided Practice

Materials two-color counters

Call attention to the green triangle on the page. Ask children to trace around the triangle with a finger. Have children use counters to complete the activity.

- **Place a counter on each vertex, or corner. How many vertices do you see?** 3
- **Write the number.**
- **Take the counters off.**
- **Place a counter on each side. What will you write for the number of sides?** 3
- **What shape has three vertices and three sides?** a triangle
- **What do you notice about the sides of this triangle?** Possible answer: They are not sides of equal length.

Discuss that a triangle has three straight sides. Review that the sides can all be the same length or different lengths, but if there are three sides it is a triangle.

Use Exercises 1 and 2 for **Quick Check**.

✔ **Quick Check** ▲ RtI

If ▶ a child misses Exercises 1 and 2

Then ▶ **Differentiate Instruction** with
- RtI Tier 1 Activity, p. 377B
- Reteach 9.6
- ⭐ Soar to Success Math 38.02

⚠️ COMMON ERRORS

Error Children may not be able to identify vertices.

Example Children do not know the number of vertices that a triangle has.

Springboard to Learning Draw a triangle. Remind children that a vertex is where two sides meet. Have children trace each side with a different color crayon. Then have them find where two sides or colors meet. Ask children to draw a dot on it. Repeat for each vertex and then count the dots.

► More Practice

Focus children's attention on the dotted grid.

Explain that they can begin on any dot as a vertex, or corner, of a triangle. Demonstrate how to draw a triangle by using three dots and connecting them. Ask them to draw and color a triangle. Remind children that the sides do not have to be the same length. Check visually.

H.O.T. Problem What is the same and different about a square and a triangle?

Possible answer: They both have straight sides and vertices. A triangle has three sides and three vertices. The sides of a triangle do not have to be the same length. A square has four sides of equal length and four vertices.

Go Deeper

Children should compare the shapes and determine that they both have straight sides and vertices but have a different number of each.

④ SUMMARIZE ⬤MATHEMATICAL PRACTICES

Essential Question

How can you describe triangles? A triangle is a shape that has three sides and three vertices.

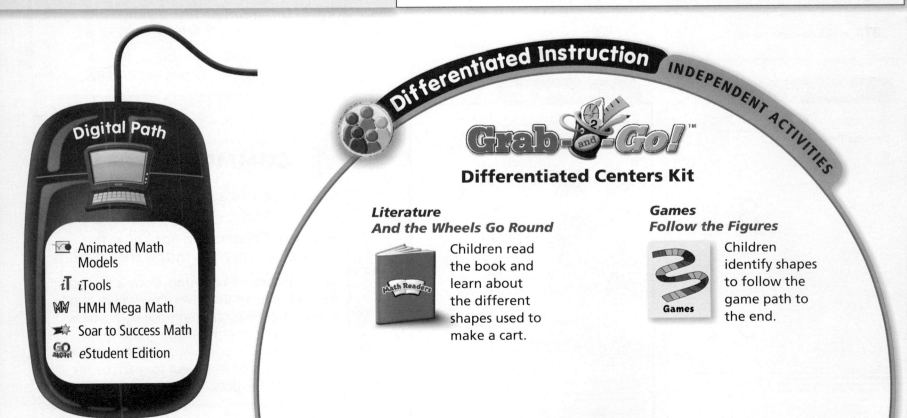

Name _____

③

Check children's work.

© Houghton Mifflin Harcourt Publishing Company

DIRECTIONS 3. Draw and color a triangle.

HOME ACTIVITY • Have your child describe a triangle.

FOR MORE PRACTICE: Standards Practice Book, pp. P181–P182

Chapter 9 • Lesson 6   **FOR EXTRA PRACTICE:** Standards Practice Book, p. P195   three hundred seventy-nine **379**

Digital Path

- ☑ Animated Math Models
- *i*T *i*Tools
- ₩₩ HMH Mega Math
- ★ Soar to Success Math
- GO eStudent Edition

Differentiated Instruction   INDEPENDENT ACTIVITIES

Grab-and-Go!™

Differentiated Centers Kit

Literature
And the Wheels Go Round

Children read the book and learn about the different shapes used to make a cart.

Games
Follow the Figures

Children identify shapes to follow the game path to the end.

✔ Mid-Chapter Checkpoint

Concepts and Skills

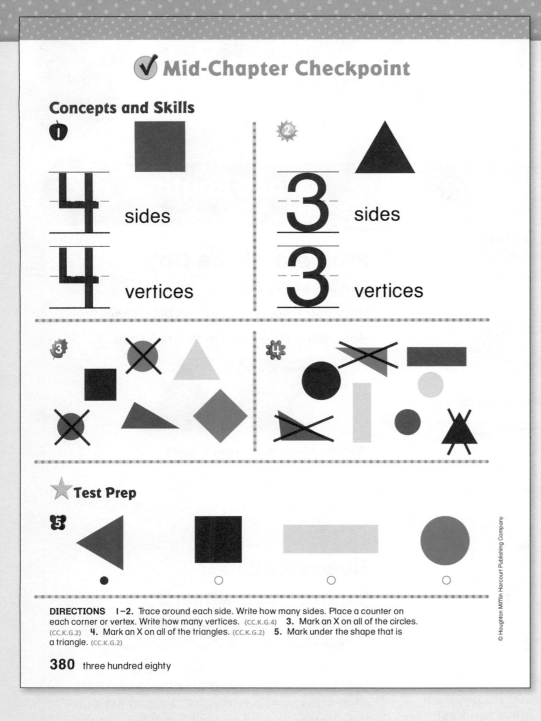

❶ **4** sides
4 vertices

❷ **3** sides
3 vertices

⭐ **Test Prep**

DIRECTIONS 1–2. Trace around each side. Write how many sides. Place a counter on each corner or vertex. Write how many vertices. (CC.K.G.4) **3.** Mark an X on all of the circles. (CC.K.G.2) **4.** Mark an X on all of the triangles. (CC.K.G.2) **5.** Mark under the shape that is a triangle. (CC.K.G.2)

© Houghton Mifflin Harcourt Publishing Company

380 three hundred eighty

Formative Assessment

Use the **Mid-Chapter Checkpoint** to assess children's learning and progress in the first half of the chapter. The formative assessment provides the opportunity to adjust teaching methods for individual or whole class instruction.

✔ Data-Driven Decision Making ▲ RtI

Based on the results of the Mid-Chapter Checkpoint, use the following resources to strengthen individual or whole class instruction.

Item	Lesson	*CCSS	Common Error	Intervene With	Soar to Success Math
1	9.4	CC.K.G.4	May have difficulty identifying sides and vertices of a square	**R**—9.4; **TE**—p. 369B	38.02
2	9.6	CC.K.G.4	May have difficulty identifying sides and vertices of a triangle	**R**—9.6; **TE**—p. 377B	38.02
3	9.1	CC.K.G.2	May have difficulty identifying circles	**R**—9.1; **TE**—p. 357B	38.02, 38.07
4, 5	9.5	CC.K.G.2	May have difficulty identifying triangles	**R**—9.5; **TE**—p. 373B	38.02, 38.07

***CCSS**—Common Core State Standards   **Key: R**—Reteach Book; **TE**—RtI Activities

Identify and Name Rectangles

LESSON AT A GLANCE

Common Core Standard
Identify and describe shapes (squares, circles, cubes, triangles, rectangles, hexagons, cubes, cones, cylinders, and spheres).
CC.K.G.2 Correctly name shapes regardless of their orientations or overall size.

Also CC.K.G.3

Materials
MathBoard, two-dimensional shapes

Lesson Objective
Identify and name two-dimensional shapes including rectangles.

Essential Question
How can you identify and name rectangles?

Vocabulary rectangle

Digital Path

iT *iTools:* Geometry

GO MATH! *eStudent Edition*

MM HMH Mega Math

PROFESSIONAL DEVELOPMENT
COMMON CORE

About the Math

Teaching for Depth

In this lesson, children sort out two-dimensional shapes that are rectangles; they identify rectangles (including squares) shown in drawings; they color and draw rectangles. To add even more depth to children's experience with rectangles, you might use activities such as the following:

• Let children predict the shapes that will result if they cut a paper rectangle diagonally from the upper left to the lower right corner, across the middle horizontally, and across the middle vertically. Have them fold the paper and make the cuts and see what results.

• Let children make designs and pictures of objects by gluing a variety of small rectangles to paper.

• Let children make crayon rubbings of the shapes and identify the rectangles.

• Have children make rectangles "dance," moving them into different positions. Emphasize that the shapes remain rectangles, no matter what positions they are in.

 Professional Development Video Podcasts

Daily Routines
Math Board

Common Core

SPIRAL REVIEW

Problem of the Day
eTransparency 9.7

Number of the Day

How many sides are on this blue shape?

How many sides are on this red shape?

Which shape has more sides?
4; 3; square

Fluency Builder

Subtract/Add within 5

Materials Subtraction Fact Cards (within 5), Addition Fact Cards (within 5) (see *eTeacher Resources*)

Display one subtraction fact card at a time. Tell a subtraction word problem to go with each equation. Invite volunteers to act out the subtraction word problems. For example, show the equation $5 - 2 = \square$.

• **Five children sit at a table. Two children leave. How many children are at the table now?** 3

Repeat with addition fact cards.

Differentiated Instruction Activities

ELL Language Support

Auditory / Kinesthetic
Small Group

Strategy: Model Concepts

Materials two-dimensional shapes

Children can learn concepts if they are modeled.

- Place several different rectangles on the table.

- Then draw a large rectangle.

- Sort and place the rectangles inside the drawing. Make sure you say *rectangle* each time you place one on the paper.

Have children repeat the activity, including naming the shape as they place it on the drawing.

See **ELL** Activity Guide for leveled activities.

Enrich

Kinesthetic
Individual / Partners

Materials Pattern Blocks (see *eTeacher Resources*)

Invite children to use pattern blocks to build rectangles of different sizes including squares.

Suggest that children place pattern blocks in different ways, such as horizontal or vertical formations. They can also use more than one row to form rectangles.

- Have children trace the different rectangles that they created to show their work. Ask them to record how many pattern blocks they used to make each rectangle.

RtI Response to Intervention

Reteach Tier 1

Visual / Kinesthetic
Whole Class / Small Group

Materials everyday objects

Ask children to trace around different kinds of objects. For example, they might trace around a can and a crayon box.

- Point to one of the tracings. **Is this a rectangle or not a rectangle?**

- Continue to point to tracings and ask children to identify the shapes that are rectangles and the shapes that are not rectangles.

- Be sure children understand that a square is a special kind of rectangle.

Tier 2

Visual / Kinesthetic
Small Group

Materials masking tape

Ahead of time, use masking tape to make outlines of rectangles and triangles on the floor. Make the outlines big enough for a child to stand in.

- Ask a volunteer to stand in a shape that is a rectangle.

- Ask another volunteer to stand in a shape that is not a rectangle.

Repeat until every child has had a chance to participate.

① ENGAGE

GO Online **iTools**

Materials iTools • Geometry

Access Prior Knowledge Show each shape: square and triangle.

Have children identify and name each shape. Then have children count the number of straight sides and vertices.

You can repeat the activity, putting the shapes in a different order.

② TEACH and TALK

GO Online HMH Mega Math

▶ **Listen and Draw** MATHEMATICAL PRACTICES

Materials two-dimensional shapes

Read aloud this problem as children listen.

Mrs. Lin has frames of all different shapes in her frame store. She wants her daughter to help sort the frames. One set of frames will be rectangles. How will her daughter know which ones are rectangles?

Give children assorted two-dimensional or flat shapes.

Help children locate and read the word *rectangles*. Hold up a rectangle and define it as a shape with four straight sides and four square vertices.

- **What other shape do you know with four straight sides and four square vertices?** square

Explain that a square is a special type of rectangle with four straight sides of equal length.

- **Look at your shapes. Find the ones that are rectangles. On the mat sort your shapes into two sets: *rectangles* and *not rectangles*.** Check visually. Squares should be included in the rectangle set.

- **Trace and color the shapes.**

- **How many shapes on the left of the sorting mat are rectangles?** all the shapes

- **How many shapes on the right of the sorting mat are rectangles?** none of the shapes

- **What is the same about all of the rectangles?** They have four straight sides and four square vertices.

- **What is different about some of the rectangles?** They have four sides of equal length.

Reread the problem.

- **How will Mrs. Lin's daughter know which frames are rectangles?** She will look for frames that have four straight sides and four square vertices.

COMMON CORE

CC.K.G.2 Correctly name shapes regardless of their orientations or overall size.

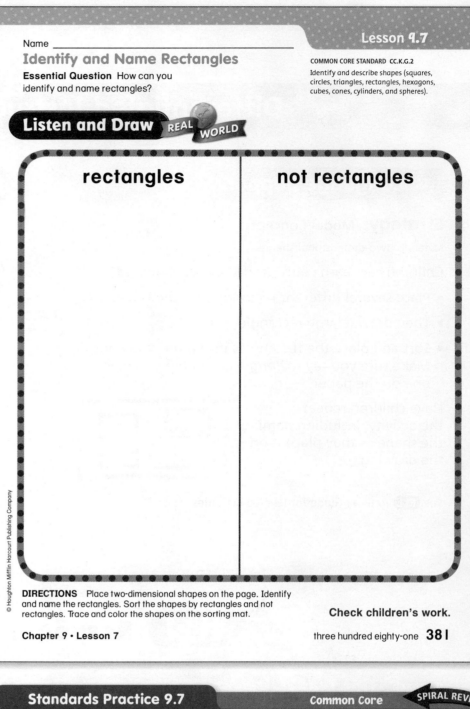

Name _____

Identify and Name Rectangles

Lesson 9.7

Essential Question How can you identify and name rectangles?

COMMON CORE STANDARD CC.K.G.2

Identify and describe shapes (squares, circles, triangles, rectangles, hexagons, cubes, cones, cylinders, and spheres).

Listen and Draw REAL WORLD

rectangles	not rectangles

© Houghton Mifflin Harcourt Publishing Company

DIRECTIONS Place two-dimensional shapes on the page. Identify and name the rectangles. Sort the shapes by rectangles and not rectangles. Trace and color the shapes on the sorting mat.

Check children's work.

Chapter 9 • Lesson 7

three hundred eighty-one **381**

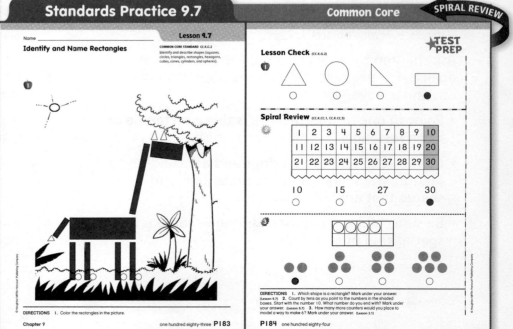

Standards Practice 9.7

Common Core

SPIRAL REVIEW

Name _____

Identify and Name Rectangles

COMMON CORE STANDARD CC.K.G.2

Identify and describe shapes (squares, circles, triangles, rectangles, hexagons, cubes, cones, cylinders, and spheres).

Lesson Check (CC.K.G.2)

TEST PREP

Spiral Review (CC.K.CC.1, CC.K.CC.5)

1	2	3	4	5	6	7	8	9	10
11	12	13	14	15	16	17	18	19	20
21	22	23	24	25	26	27	28	29	30

10   15   27   30

DIRECTIONS 1. Which shape is a rectangle? Mark under your answer. (Lesson 9.7) 2. Count by tens as you point to the numbers in the shaded boxes. Start with the number 10. What number do you end with? Mark under your answer. (Lesson 8.7) 3. How many more counters would you place to model a way to make 6? Mark under your answer. (Lesson 3.1)

DIRECTIONS 1. Color the rectangles in the picture.

Chapter 9

one hundred eighty-three **P183**

P184 one hundred eighty-four

Share and Show

▶ **Share and Show** • Guided Practice

Discuss the shapes on the page for Exercise 1.

- **Are all the shapes the same?** no
- **Can you name some of the shapes you see?** triangles, circles, trapezoid, hexagons, and rectangles

Have children find all of the rectangles and then mark an X on all of the rectangles on the page. Remind children to mark squares as rectangles.

- **How many rectangles did you find?** 7
- **Do all of the rectangles look the same?** no
- **What is the same about the rectangles?** They all have four straight sides and four square vertices.
- **What is different about the rectangles?** size, color, and position; some rectangles are squares

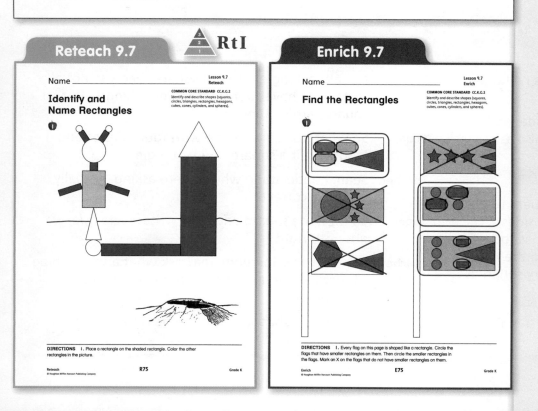

COMMON ERRORS

Error Children may not recognize squares as rectangles.

Example Children do not mark the squares.

Springboard to Learning Have children trace a rectangle and count the sides, four. Then have them count the sides for each shape. Have them say *rectangle* when they count four sides.

► More Practice

Invite children to tell what they see in the picture in Exercise 2.

- **What do you see in the picture?** an animal and some trees

Discuss which shapes are used for different parts of the picture.

Ask children to find the shapes that are rectangles and then color them.

Use Exercise 2 for **Quick Check**.

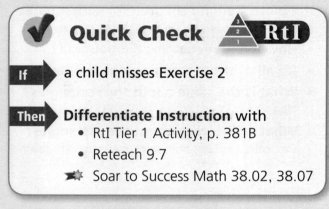

Quick Check RtI

If → a child misses Exercise 2

Then → **Differentiate Instruction** with
- RtI Tier 1 Activity, p. 381B
- Reteach 9.7
- ✦ Soar to Success Math 38.02, 38.07

H.O.T. Problem Are there more rectangles or triangles? rectangles **How many more?** five more

Go Deeper
MATHEMATICAL PRACTICES

Children will need to distinguish between different shapes and then use what they know about comparing to determine which set has more.

Name _____

© Houghton Mifflin Harcourt Publishing Company

DIRECTIONS 2. Color the rectangles in the picture.

Chapter 9 • Lesson 7   three hundred eighty-three **383**

COMMON CORE
PROFESSIONAL DEVELOPMENT

Math Talk in Action

Sally: You drew a square, but you said it was a rectangle. I am confused!

Teacher: Yes, I drew a square. It has four straight sides and all the sides are of equal length. But it is also a rectangle.

Sally: It is? Really?

Teacher: Yes, Sally, it is. I drew a square, but a square is a special kind of rectangle that has four sides of equal length. You know a rectangle has four straight sides and four square corners, so the square I drew is a rectangle. In fact, every square is a special kind of rectangle.

Sally: Are all rectangles squares?

Teacher: No, all rectangles are not squares because not all rectangles have four sides of equal length. But all squares are rectangles.

Sean: So what do I call a shape with four sides of equal length? Is it a square or a rectangle?

Teacher: Sean, I understand why you are asking. Actually, both are correct.

Sean: So if I write *square* and Sally writes *rectangle,* we are both right?

Teacher: Yes, you are. Someone may ask what a special type of rectangle is, and then the answer would be a square.

Sean: That is cool that we can both be right!

PROBLEM SOLVING

Check children's work.

DIRECTIONS 1. Which shapes are rectangles? Mark an X on those shapes.
2. Draw to show what you know about rectangles. Tell a friend about your drawing.

HOME ACTIVITY • Have your child show you an object that is shaped like a rectangle.

© Houghton Mifflin Harcourt Publishing Company

384 three hundred eighty-four

FOR MORE PRACTICE:
Standards Practice Book, pp. P183–P184

▶ **Problem Solving**

Read the problem and discuss how to complete it.

- **How many green shapes do you see?** 5
- **Are they all rectangles?** no
- **How many rectangles are there?** 2
- **How do you know which ones are rectangles?** They have four straight sides.

Before they show what they know about rectangles, guide children to say that a rectangle has four straight sides that can be the same lengths or different lengths. Have children tell a friend about their drawing.

After children draw, have them take turns showing their completed drawings.

4 SUMMARIZE

Essential Question

How can you identify and name rectangles?
I know that a rectangle is a shape with four straight sides and four square vertices.

Differentiated Instruction — INDEPENDENT ACTIVITIES

Grab-and-Go!
Differentiated Centers Kit

Literature
I Know Shapes

Children read the book and identify circles, squares, rectangles, and triangles.

Games
Number Picture

Children identify and color two-dimensional shapes to complete a picture.

Digital Path
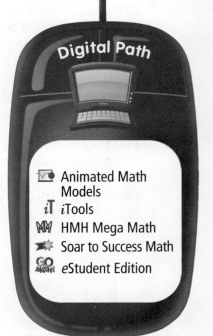

- Animated Math Models
- *i*Tools
- HMH Mega Math
- Soar to Success Math
- *e*Student Edition

Describe Rectangles

LESSON AT A GLANCE

Common Core Standard
Analyze, compare, create, and compose shapes.
CC.K.G.4 Analyze and compare two- and three-dimensional shapes, in different sizes and orientations, using informal language to describe their similarities, differences, parts (e.g., number of sides and vertices/"corners") and other attributes (e.g., having sides of equal length).

Also CC.K.G.2, CC.K.G.5

Lesson Objective
Describe attributes of rectangles.

Essential Question
How can you describe rectangles?

Materials
MathBoard, two-color counters

Digital Path

iT **iTools:** Geometry

GO **eStudent Edition**

MM **HMH Mega Math**

COMMON CORE PROFESSIONAL DEVELOPMENT — About the Math

If Children Ask

Perhaps a child asks, "Is a square a rectangle?" Or maybe a child calls a square a rectangle.

A square is a rectangle—a special rectangle. A square has all the attributes of a rectangle—both are closed shapes with four straight sides and four right angles. However, the sides of a square are of equal length; that makes the square a unique kind of rectangle. Most people easily recognize a rectangle with two pairs of equal sides; all four sides need not be equal in length. Squares form a subset of rectangles.

You might tell the children that each of them has a special name. Each could be called a boy or a girl, but they also have special names—Amy, Scott, Carlos, or Janie. In the same way, a square is a special rectangle and we usually call it by its special name—a square.

PODCASTING **Professional Development Video Podcasts**

Daily Routines
Math Board

SPIRAL REVIEW Common Core

Problem of the Day
eTransparency 9.8

Number of the Day How many rectangles are shown? What is special about the purple rectangle?

4; It is a square.

As children count the rectangles, remind them that the orientation of the shape does not change the name of the shape.

Fluency Builder
Counting to 100 by Tens

Materials Hundred Chart (see *eTeacher Resources*)

Display the hundred chart. Lead children in counting from 10 to 100 by tens.

Ask a volunteer to point to the hundred chart as you ask the following questions.

- **When you count by tens, what number comes after 30?** 40 **Count forward from 30 to 100 by tens.**

- **When you count by tens, what number comes after 80?** 90 **Count forward from 80 to 100 by tens.**

- **Repeat the activity with different numbers.**

Differentiated Instruction Activities

ELL Language Support
🕐 Visual / Auditory · Small Group

Strategy: Identify Relationships

Materials Two-Dimensional Shapes (see *eTeacher Resources*)

Children can understand language by making connections between new information and prior knowledge.

- Have children identify the number of sides and vertices on a square and on a rectangle that is not a square.

- **How are the sides of the blue square and the yellow rectangle the same?** They both have four straight sides. **How are they different?** The sides of the square are the same length.

See **ELL** Activity Guide for leveled activities.

Enrich
🕐 Kinesthetic · Individual / Partner

Materials Two-Dimensional Shapes (see *eTeacher Resources*), crayons, paper

Give each child a square and a rectangle. Have them trace the shapes on a piece of paper.

- Have children count the number of sides for each shape and write the number below the shape. 4

- Have children use different colored crayons to color the sides that have the same length.

- Then have children think of how the two shapes would look if they were turned. Ask them to draw what the turned shapes would look like.

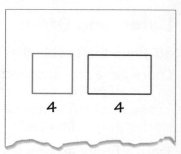

▲ RtI Response to Intervention

Reteach Tier 1
🕐 Visual / Kinesthetic · Whole Class / Small Group

Materials construction paper cut into rectangles and triangles, tape

Draw a large rectangle and a triangle on the board. Label each.

- Give each child a small paper rectangle and a triangle. Children should tape each shape inside the matching shape on the board. Have children say the name of their shape as they tape it to the board.

- **How did you know which shapes were rectangles?** Rectangles have four sides and four square vertices.

- **How did you know which shapes were triangles?** Triangles have three sides and three vertices.

Tier 2
🕐 Visual / Kinesthetic · Small Group

Materials chart paper, marker

Draw a rectangle on chart paper. Trace it with a finger. **What is this shape?** a rectangle

- Point to and count the four sides, and then count the four vertices of the rectangle. Ask children to count the sides and vertices with you. **How many square vertices does a rectangle have?** 4 **How many sides does a rectangle have?** 4

Give children an opportunity to trace the rectangle on the chart paper with a finger.

1 ENGAGE Math Board

Materials clay, straws (some cut in half)

Access Prior Knowledge Have children make models of rectangles using clay and straws. Help children select two short straws and two long straws or four straws of the same length.

- **Roll the clay into four small balls for the corners or vertices. Press the ends of four straws into the clay to form a rectangle.**

- **What shape do you have?** a rectangle

- **How do you know it is a rectangle?** It has four straight sides and four square vertices.

- **My rectangle has four sides of the same length. Is it still a rectangle? Explain.** Yes. It is a square. A square is a special kind of rectangle.

2 TEACH and TALK GO Online iTools

▶ **Listen and Draw** MATHEMATICAL PRACTICES

Read aloud this problem as children listen.

Chuck has a stamp collection. He wants to put all of the stamps that are rectangles in one book. How will he know which stamps are rectangles?

- **Trace a finger around the rectangle. Find the worm sitting on the side and the word *side*.**

- **How many sides does the rectangle have?** 4

- **Are all of the sides of equal length?** no **Describe the sides.** There are two long sides and two short sides.

- **Trace around the sides.**

Remind children that the word *vertex* means "corner."

- **Find the worm sitting on the vertex and the word *vertex*. How many vertices does the rectangle have?** 4

- **Draw an arrow pointing to another vertex.**

Be sure to tell children that a square is a special type of rectangle because it also has four straight sides and four vertices, but the sides are all of equal length.

Reread the problem.

- **How will Chuck know which stamps are rectangles?** The stamps that have four straight sides and four square vertices are rectangles.

COMMON CORE

CC.K.G.4 Analyze and compare two- and three-dimensional shapes, in different sizes and orientations, using informal language to describe their similarities, differences, parts (e.g., number of sides and vertices/"corners") and other attributes (e.g., having sides of equal length).

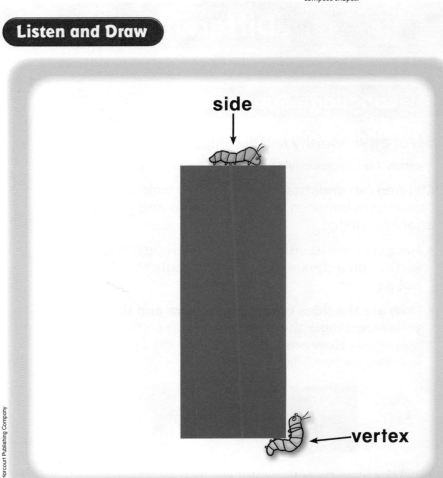

Name _____

Lesson 9.8

Describe Rectangles

COMMON CORE STANDARD CC.K.G.4
Analyze, compare, create, and compose shapes.

Essential Question How can you describe rectangles?

Listen and Draw

side

vertex

DIRECTIONS Use your finger to trace around the rectangle. Talk about the number of sides and the number of vertices. Draw an arrow pointing to another vertex. Trace around the sides.

Chapter 9 • Lesson 8

Check children's work.

three hundred eighty-five **385**

© Houghton Mifflin Harcourt Publishing Company

Standards Practice 9.8 **Common Core** SPIRAL REVIEW

Name _____ Lesson 9.8
Describe Rectangles

COMMON CORE STANDARD CC.K.G.4
Analyze, compare, create, and compose shapes.

Check children's work.

4 vertices 4 sides

DIRECTIONS 1. Draw and color a rectangle. 2. Place a counter on each corner, or vertex, of the rectangle that you drew. Write how many corners, or vertices. 3. Trace around the sides of the rectangle that you drew. Write how many sides.

Chapter 9 one hundred eighty-five **P185**

Lesson Check (CC.K.G.4) ★TEST PREP

1

  1   2   3   4
  ○   ○   ○   ●

Spiral Review (CC.K.CC.6, CC.K.OA.2)

2

● 6 + 3 = 9   ○ 8 − 3 = 5
○ 7 + 2 = 9   ○ 9 − 4 = 5

3

  ○   ○   ○   ●

DIRECTIONS 1. How many sides does the rectangle have? Mark under your answer. (Lesson 9.8) 2. Mark beside the number sentence that matches the picture. (Lesson 6.7) 3. Compare the sets. Which set has a number of cubes two greater than 18? Mark under your answer. (Lesson 8.4)

P186 one hundred eighty-six

Share and Show

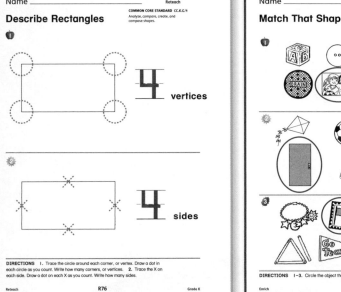

rectangle

Check children's work.

· ·

🍎 ✓ **4** vertices

· ·

② ✓ **4** sides

· ·

DIRECTIONS 1. Place a counter on each corner, or vertex. Write how many corners, or vertices. **2.** Trace around the sides. Write how many sides.

386 three hundred eighty-six

▶ **Share and Show** • Guided Practice

Materials two-color counters

Call attention to the red rectangle on the page. Ask children to trace around the rectangle with a finger.

• **Place a counter on each vertex, or corner, of the rectangle. How many vertices do you see?** 4 **Write the number.**

• **Trace around each side of the rectangle. What number will you write?** 4 **Why?** because a rectangle has four straight sides

Review with children that this rectangle has four vertices and four sides. Some children may note that two of the sides are long and two are short.

• **Does a rectangle have the same number of vertices and sides as a square?** yes **How many vertices and sides do they each have?** 4

Elicit that the square is also a rectangle because is has four sides and four vertices. Help children see that a square is a special kind of rectangle—one with four sides of equal length.

Use Exercises 1 and 2 for **Quick Check**.

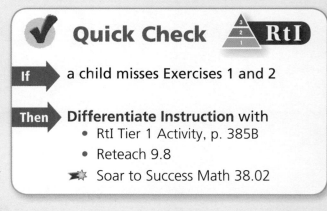

Quick Check [RtI]

If → a child misses Exercises 1 and 2

Then → **Differentiate Instruction** with
• RtI Tier 1 Activity, p. 385B
• Reteach 9.8
• Soar to Success Math 38.02

⚠ COMMON ERRORS

Error Children may not be able to identify a vertex.

Example Children cannot tell the number of vertices.

Springboard to Learning Draw a rectangle. Have children start at a vertex and place a counter there. Then ask them to place another counter each time they turn or change directions with their finger while tracing the shape. Have children count the counters to see how many vertices.

Reteach 9.8 [RtI]

Name _____
Lesson 9.8
Reteach

Describe Rectangles
COMMON CORE STANDARD CC.K.G.4
Analyze, compare, create, and compose shapes.

❶
4 vertices

4 sides

DIRECTIONS 1. Trace the circle around each corner, or vertex. Draw a dot in each circle as you count. Write how many corners, or vertices. **2.** Trace the X on each side. Draw a dot on each X as you count. Write how many sides.

Reteach   R76   Grade K
© Houghton Mifflin Harcourt Publishing Company

Enrich 9.8

Name _____
Lesson 9.8
Enrich

Match That Shape
COMMON CORE STANDARD CC.K.G.4
Analyze, compare, create, and compose shapes.

❶
Children should draw a rectangle with two children in it.

②
Children should draw a rectangular door.

③
Children should draw a rectangular stamp.

DIRECTIONS 1–3. Circle the object that is a rectangle. Draw the object.

Enrich   E76   Grade K
© Houghton Mifflin Harcourt Publishing Company

▶ More Practice

Demonstrate how to draw a rectangle by marking four dots and then connecting them. Point out how to align the dots across and up and down so that when they are joined they would make two long sides of equal length and two short sides of equal length. If a child draws a square, reinforce that a square is a special kind of rectangle.

- **How many vertices, or corners, does a rectangle have?** 4 **How many sides does a rectangle have?** 4

Ask children to draw and color a rectangle. After children finish their drawings, have them compare them. Point out that rectangles can have two long and two short sides, or four sides of equal length.

H.O.T. Problem Give children strips of construction paper for two long sides equal in length and two short sides equal in length. Ask children to use them to make a rectangle.

Go Deeper

Have children describe the sides of the rectangle that they made. Elicit that there are not only two long and two short sides, but opposite sides are equal in length to each other.

Name _____

DIRECTIONS 3. Draw and color a rectangle.

Check children's work.

Chapter 9 · Lesson 8   three hundred eighty-seven **387**

PROBLEM SOLVING

Check children's work.

DIRECTIONS I have 4 sides and 4 vertices. What shape am I? Draw the shape. Tell a friend the name of the shape.

HOME ACTIVITY • Have your child describe a rectangle.

FOR MORE PRACTICE: Standards Practice Book, pp. P185–P186

▶ **Problem Solving**

Read the riddle for the children. Ask children to explain how they will solve the riddle.

- **What shape has four sides?** a rectangle
- **What shape has four vertices?** a rectangle
- **What shape will you draw?** a rectangle

Invite children to draw a rectangle and then share and compare the number of sides in their rectangles. Then have children compare the number of vertices in their rectangles. Have children compare their rectangles with a friend and discuss similarities and differences. Note that some children may draw squares.

4 SUMMARIZE

Essential Question

How can you describe rectangles? I know that a rectangle is a shape that has four straight sides and four square vertices.

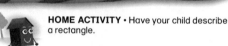

Differentiated Centers Kit

Literature
I Know Shapes

Children read the book and identify circles, squares, rectangles, and triangles.

Games
Number Picture

Children identify and color two-dimensional shapes to complete a picture.

Digital Path

- Animated Math Models
- *i*Tools
- HMH Mega Math
- Soar to Success Math
- *e*Student Edition

Lesson 9.8   388

Identify and Name Hexagons

LESSON AT A GLANCE

Common Core Standard
Identify and describe shapes (squares, circles, triangles, rectangles, hexagons, cubes, cones, cylinders, and spheres.
CC.K.G.2 Correctly name shapes regardless of their orientations or overall size.

Also CC.K.G.3

Materials
MathBoard, two-dimensional shapes

Lesson Objective
Identify and name two-dimensional shapes including hexagons.

Essential Question
How can you identify and name hexagons?

Vocabulary **hexagon**

Digital Path

iT **iTools: Geometry**

MM **HMH Mega Math**

eStudent Edition

PROFESSIONAL DEVELOPMENT COMMON CORE

About the Math

Teaching for Depth

Most of the two-dimensional shapes that children have seen so far have been circles and regular polygons. You may want to help children see that the attributes they have learned for identifying polygons apply to irregular polygons as well. Draw hexagons like these on the board.

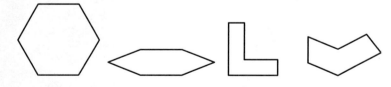

Ask children how many of these shapes are hexagons. Children may say that only the first shape is a hexagon. Have volunteers come to the board and count the sides. Explain that the sides of a hexagon do not need to be of equal length, so all of those shapes are hexagons.

Professional Development Video Podcasts

Daily Routines
Math Board

Common Core

SPIRAL REVIEW

Problem of the Day

eTransparency
9.9

Word of the Day *same*
Are these shapes the same?
How are they the same?
What is the name of this shape?

Possible answer: Yes; They are the same size, color, and shape; rectangle

---

Fluency Builder

Add/Subtract within 5

Materials connecting cubes, Addition Fact Cards (within 5), Subtraction Fact Cards (within 5) (see *eTeacher Resources*)

Display one addition fact card at a time. Tell an addition word problem to go with each equation. Invite volunteers to show each addition word problem using cubes. For example, show the equation $1 + 4 = \square$.

- **Dan has 1 red cube and 4 blue cubes. How many cubes does Dan have in all?** 5

- Repeat with subtraction fact cards.

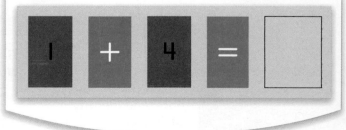

Differentiated Instruction Activities

ELL Language Support
🕐 Kinesthetic
Small Group

Strategy: Draw

Materials paper, crayons

Children can demonstrate their understanding by drawing rather than by using language.

- Show children a hexagon, a rectangle, and a circle. Have children identify the hexagon.

- Ask children to draw a picture using each of these shapes. Tell children they can use the shapes more than once.

- Have children present their pictures to the group and name the shapes they used.

See **ELL** Activity Guide for leveled activities.

Enrich
🕐 Kinesthetic
Individual / Partners

Materials magazines, catalogs, safety scissors, glue, construction paper

Ahead of time, label sheets of construction paper with headings such as: Circles, Rectangles, Hexagons, and so on. Give each set of partners a set of labeled sheets.

- Each child searches the catalogs and magazines to find examples of objects that model the two-dimensional shape written on the top of their paper. They might find picture frames for the squares, doors for rectangles, and rings for circle shapes.

- Have children make a poster for each shape by gluing the pictures on the construction paper.

RtI Response to Intervention

Reteach Tier 1
🕐 Kinesthetic / Visual
Whole Class / Small Group

Show the class a large square, triangle, and hexagon. Display the shapes at the front of the classroom.

- Ask children to put the shapes in order from the one with the least number of sides to the one with the greatest number of sides. For each shape, have children say: **A _____ has _____ sides.** triangle, 3: square, 4; hexagon, 6

- Then ask children to name the shape that has six sides. Have them describe how a hexagon is different from the other shapes. Possible answer: A hexagon has six sides.

Tier 2
🕐 Visual / Kinesthetic
Small Group

Materials two-dimensional shapes

Display three triangles and one hexagon.

- Ask what the shapes are called. triangles, hexagon Have children tell how they decided what the names of the shapes were. Then ask volunteers to tell which shape does not belong and explain why. Possible answer: the hexagon; it has more sides than the triangles. Have the group discuss each answer and decide whether it is correct. Encourage children who have different ideas to present so the group can discuss them.

- Repeat for three hexagons and one square.

1 ENGAGE

Access Prior Knowledge Draw a puppet shape on the board with a circle for the head, a rectangle for the body, squares for the legs, and a triangle for a hat.

- **What shape is the puppet's head?** a circle
- **What shape is the puppet's body?** a rectangle
- **What shape is the puppet's legs?** squares, or rectangles
- **What shape is the puppet's hat?** a triangle

2 TEACH and TALK GO Online iTools

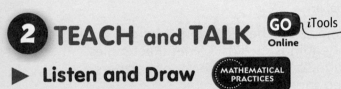

▶ **Listen and Draw** MATHEMATICAL PRACTICES

Materials two-dimensional shapes

Read aloud this problem as children listen.

Nadine has a picture collection of different shapes. She wants to sort out all of the hexagons. How will Nadine know which shapes are hexagons?

Help children locate and read the word *hexagons*.

Hold up a hexagon and identify a side. Then point to and count each of the six sides.

- **Hexagons have six straight sides. Trace each side of the hexagon with a finger and count 1, 2, 3, 4, 5, 6.**

Give children assorted two-dimensional shapes. Read the labels on the sorting mat. Then have children sort out the hexagons, identifying and naming them as they are sorted.

- **Look at your shapes. Sort them on the mat into sets:** *hexagons* and *not hexagons.* **Trace and color the shapes.**
- **How many shapes on the left of the sorting mat are hexagons?** all of the shapes
- **How many shapes on the right of the sorting mat are hexagons?** none of the shapes
- **What is the same about the hexagons?** They have six straight sides.

Reread the problem.

- **How will Nadine know which shapes are hexagons?** She can find the shapes that have six straight sides.

COMMON CORE CC.K.G.2 Correctly name shapes regardless of their orientations or overall size.

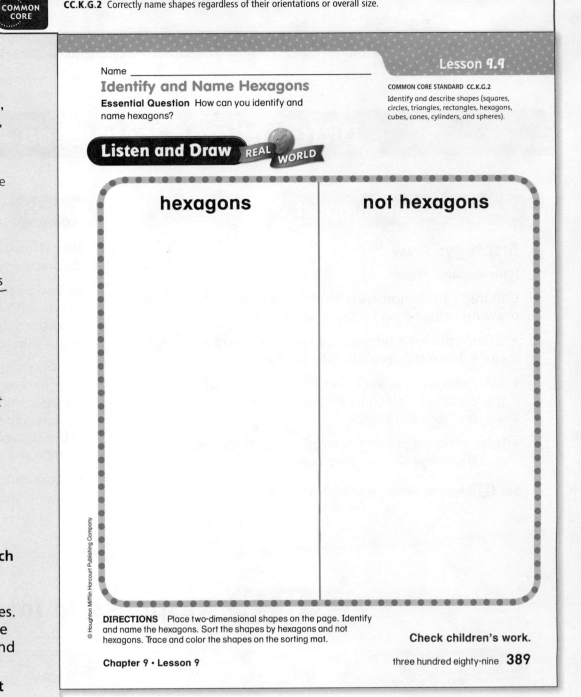

Name _____

Identify and Name Hexagons

Essential Question How can you identify and name hexagons?

Lesson 9.9

COMMON CORE STANDARD CC.K.G.2
Identify and describe shapes (squares, circles, triangles, rectangles, hexagons, cubes, cones, cylinders, and spheres).

Listen and Draw REAL WORLD

hexagons	not hexagons

DIRECTIONS Place two-dimensional shapes on the page. Identify and name the hexagons. Sort the shapes by hexagons and not hexagons. Trace and color the shapes on the sorting mat.

Check children's work.

Chapter 9 • Lesson 9

three hundred eighty-nine **389**

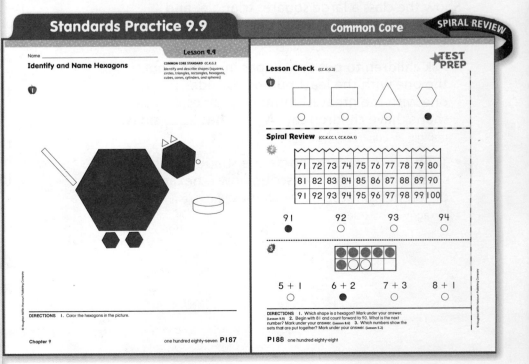

Standards Practice 9.9 Common Core SPIRAL REVIEW

Name _____

Identify and Name Hexagons

COMMON CORE STANDARD CC.K.G.2
Identify and describe shapes (squares, circles, triangles, rectangles, hexagons, cubes, cones, cylinders, and spheres).

Lesson Check (CC.K.G.2)

Spiral Review (CC.K.CC.1, CC.K.OA.1)

71	72	73	74	75	76	77	78	79	80
81	82	83	84	85	86	87	88	89	90
91	92	93	94	95	96	97	98	99	100

91   92   93   94

5 + 1   6 + 2   7 + 3   8 + 1

DIRECTIONS 1. Color the hexagons in the picture.

DIRECTIONS 1. Which shape is a hexagon? Mark under your answer. (Lesson 9.9) 2. Begin with 81 and count forward to 90. What is the next number? Mark under your answer. (Lesson 8.5) 3. Which numbers show the sets that are put together? Mark under your answer. (Lesson 5.2)

Chapter 9   one hundred eighty-seven **P187**

P188 one hundred eighty-eight

Share and Show

DIRECTIONS 1. Mark an X on all of the hexagons.

---

3 PRACTICE Math Board

▶ **Share and Show** • Guided Practice

Call attention to the shapes on the page.

- **Look at the shapes on the page. Are all of the shapes the same?** no
- **Can you name any of the shapes?** Children may name circles, squares, rectangles, triangles, and hexagons.
- **Are any of the shapes hexagons?** yes
- **How do you know which shapes are hexagons?** The hexagons are the shapes with six straight sides.

Have children find all of the hexagons and then mark them with an X.

- **How many hexagons did you find?** 4

Reteach 9.9 ▲ RtI

Name _____

Identify and Name Hexagons

COMMON CORE STANDARD CC.K.G.2
Identify and describe shapes (squares, circles, triangles, rectangles, hexagons, cubes, cones, cylinders, and spheres).

Lesson 9.9
Reteach

DIRECTIONS 1. Place a hexagon on the shaded hexagon. Color the other hexagons in the picture.

Reteach
© Houghton Mifflin Harcourt Publishing Company
R77
Grade K

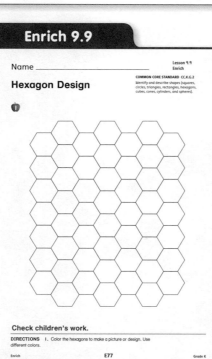

Enrich 9.9

Name _____

Hexagon Design

COMMON CORE STANDARD CC.K.G.2
Identify and describe shapes (squares, circles, triangles, rectangles, hexagons, cubes, cones, cylinders, and spheres).

Lesson 9.9
Enrich

Check children's work.

DIRECTIONS 1. Color the hexagons to make a picture or design. Use different colors.

Enrich
© Houghton Mifflin Harcourt Publishing Company
E77
Grade K

⚠ COMMON ERRORS

Error Children may not be able to keep track of the number of sides as they count.

Example Children count five sides instead of six for a hexagon.

Springboard to Learning Have children place a small pencil mark on each side of the hexagon as they count the sides.

► More Practice

Talk about the picture shown on the page. Have children find the hexagon shapes. Remind children that a hexagon is a two-dimensional (or flat) shape with six straight sides.

- **Color the hexagon shapes.**
- **How many hexagons did you color?** 5

Use Exercise 2 for **Quick Check**.

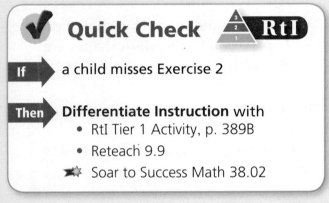

Quick Check

If a child misses Exercise 2

Then **Differentiate Instruction** with
- RtI Tier 1 Activity, p. 389B
- Reteach 9.9
- Soar to Success Math 38.02

H.O.T. Problem How are the hexagons different from the other shapes in the picture?
The hexagons have six sides. The other shapes do not.

Go Deeper

MATHEMATICAL PRACTICES

Have children draw their own pictures using outlines of circles, hexagons, and other shapes. Have children work with a partner to name the shapes in the picture.

Name _____

© Houghton Mifflin Harcourt Publishing Company

DIRECTIONS   2. Color the hexagons in the picture.

Chapter 9 • Lesson 9   three hundred ninety-one **391**

PROBLEM SOLVING

①

②

Check children's work.

DIRECTIONS I. Which shapes are hexagons? Mark an X on those shapes. **2.** Draw to show what you know about hexagons. Tell a friend about your drawing.

HOME ACTIVITY • Draw some shapes on a page. Include several hexagons. Have your child circle the hexagons.

© Houghton Mifflin Harcourt Publishing Company

FOR MORE PRACTICE: Standards Practice Book, pp. P187–P188

▶ **Problem Solving**

Have children look at Exercise 1. Ask them to explain how they will solve the problem.

- **How many shapes do you see?** 5
- **Are they all hexagons?** no
- **How many hexagons are there?** 2 **Mark an X on the hexagons.**

Before children draw to show what they know about a hexagon for Exercise 2, ask them to tell what they know. Guide children to describe a hexagon as a shape that has six straight sides.

When children have completed this page, they may wish to place it in a Math Journal.

4 SUMMARIZE

Essential Question

How can you identify and name hexagons?
I know a hexagon is a shape with six straight sides.

Differentiated Instruction — INDEPENDENT ACTIVITIES

Grab-and-Go!
Differentiated Centers Kit

Literature
I Know Shapes

Children read the book and identify circles, squares, rectangles, and triangles.

Games
Number Picture

Children identify and color two-dimensional shapes to complete a picture.

Digital Path

- Animated Math Models
- iT iTools
- HMH Mega Math
- Soar to Success Math
- eStudent Edition

Describe Hexagons

LESSON AT A GLANCE

Common Core Standard

Analyze, compare, create, and compose shapes.
CC.K.G.4 Analyze and compare two- and three-dimensional shapes, in different sizes and orientations, using informal language to describe their similarities, differences, parts (e.g., number of sides and vertices/"corners") and other attributes (e.g., having sides of equal length).

Also CC.K.G.2, CC.K.G.5

Lesson Objective

Describe attributes of hexagons.

Essential Question

How can you describe hexagons?

Materials

MathBoard, two-color counters

Digital Path

iT *i*Tools: Geometry

HMH Mega Math

eStudent Edition

PROFESSIONAL DEVELOPMENT
COMMON CORE

About the Math

Teaching for Depth

Give small groups of children straws of various lengths and small balls of clay. Demonstrate how to make a hexagon using six straws and six balls of clay as children follow along.

Children studied some simple geometric shapes in this chapter. Solidify their understanding with an investigation of similarities and differences among these shapes.

Ask them to make models of a triangle, a square, a rectangle, and a hexagon by using the straws as sides and balls of clay as vertices. Have groups present and discuss their shapes.

Bring out points like the following during the discussions: Is a square a rectangle? How are these shapes different from circles? Are all these shapes flat shapes? How is a hexagon different from a triangle?

 Professional Development Video Podcasts

Problem of the Day

eTransparency 9.10

Number of the Day teen numbers

What number is 10 ones and 5 more?
What number is 10 ones and 7 more?
Describe the number 18.
15; 17; 10 ones and 8 more ones

Continue with other numbers from 11 to 19.

Fluency Builder

Counting Tape

Materials Counting Tape

Continue to update daily. Frequently count by tens and ones to help children become comfortable reading greater numbers. Ask a variety of questions such as the following to challenge each student.

• **Yesterday you wrote the number 116. What number will you write today?** 117

• **What number will you write tomorrow?** 118

• **How many more days until you get another pair of hands?** 3

• **What number day will that be?** 120

• **Which number is greater, 8 or 10?** 10

• **Which number is less, 12 or 7?** 7

• **What are the number neighbors for 17?** 16, 18

• **What are the number neighbors for 117?** 116, 118

Differentiated Instruction Activities

ELL Language Support | Kinesthetic Small Group

Strategy: Model Language

Children can learn correct pronunciation and sentence structure by repeating words and sentences that are modeled by a native speaker.

- When you describe a hexagon, have children repeat each of these sentences: **Hexagons have six sides. Hexagons have six vertices.**

- Have children draw a hexagon.

- Ask children to share their drawings.

See **ELL** Activity Guide for leveled activities.

Enrich | Kinesthetic Individual / Partners

Materials crayons

Have children trace all of these shapes onto paper: circle, square, triangle, rectangle, and hexagon.

- Have children color all the circles red, all of the triangles green, all of the squares yellow, all of the rectangles purple, and all of the hexagons blue.

- Have children exchange their drawings with a partner and identify the shapes in their partner's drawing.

RtI Response to Intervention

Reteach Tier 1 | Kinesthetic / Visual Whole Class / Small Group

Materials two-dimensional shapes

Draw a hexagon on the board.

- Have a volunteer trace around the hexagon. **How many sides does the shape have?** 6 Have children count the sides as you point to them. **This shape has six sides. It is a hexagon.**

- **How many vertices or corners does the hexagon have?** 6

- Then draw a triangle on the board. **How many sides does this shape have?** 3 **How many vertices does it have?** 3 **What is its name?** triangle

- Have children discuss how these shapes are the same and different.

Tier 2 | Visual / Kinesthetic Small Group

Materials masking tape, two-dimensional shapes

Tape an outline of a hexagon on the floor.

- Have children walk around the hexagon. **How many sides does the shape have?** 6 **How many vertices or corners does the shape have?** 6 **What is the name of the shape?** hexagon

- Then tape an outline of a square on the floor and have children walk around it. **How many sides does the shape have?** 4 **How many vertices does it have?** 4 **What is its name?** square

- Then have each child select a two-dimensional shape. Have children find the shape on the floor that matches their shape and stand on or near it.

1 ENGAGE Math Board

Access Prior Knowledge Draw the following on the board in a row: a triangle and a rectangle.

- **On your MathBoard, draw these two shapes. What are the names of the shapes?** triangle, rectangle
- **Count the straight sides in these shapes and write the number of straight sides in the center of the shape.** three in the triangle, four in the rectangle

2 TEACH and TALK GO Online iTools

▶ **Listen and Draw** MATHEMATICAL PRACTICES

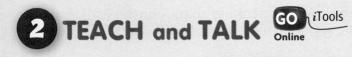

Read aloud this problem as children listen.

Carol is missing a shape for her puzzle. She wants her brother to guess what shape she is missing. She gives him a clue: "My shape has six sides and six vertices." What shape is Carol missing from her puzzle?

Have children look at the hexagon on the page.

- **Trace around the hexagon with your finger. Find the worm sitting on the side and the word *side*.**
- **How many sides does the hexagon have?** 6

Point to a corner and review that a corner is where two sides meet. Remind children that the word *vertex* is another name for corner and the word *vertices* is used to name more than one vertex.

- **Find the worm sitting on the vertex and the word *vertex*.**
- **How many vertices, or corners, does the hexagon have?** 6
- **Trace around the sides of the hexagon.**
- **Draw an arrow pointing to another vertex.**

Reread the problem.

- **What shape is Carol missing?** a hexagon
- **How do you know?** Carol's clue was that the shape has six sides and six vertices. A hexagon has six sides and six vertices.

COMMON CORE

CC.K.G.4 Analyze and compare two- and three-dimensional shapes, in different sizes and orientations, using informal language to describe their similarities, differences, parts (e.g., number of sides and vertices/"corners") and other attributes (e.g., having 9 sides of equal length).

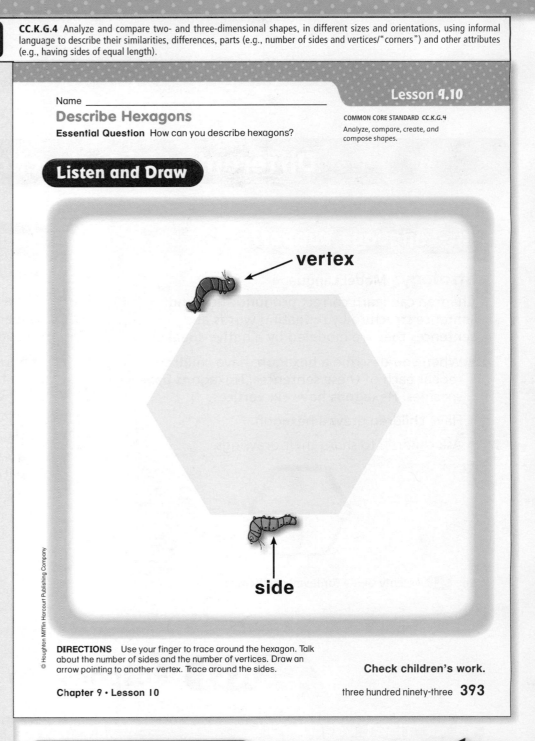

Name _____

Describe Hexagons

Essential Question How can you describe hexagons?

Lesson 9.10

COMMON CORE STANDARD CC.K.G.4
Analyze, compare, create, and compose shapes.

Listen and Draw

vertex

side

DIRECTIONS Use your finger to trace around the hexagon. Talk about the number of sides and the number of vertices. Draw an arrow pointing to another vertex. Trace around the sides.

Chapter 9 • Lesson 10

© Houghton Mifflin Harcourt Publishing Company

Check children's work.

three hundred ninety-three **393**

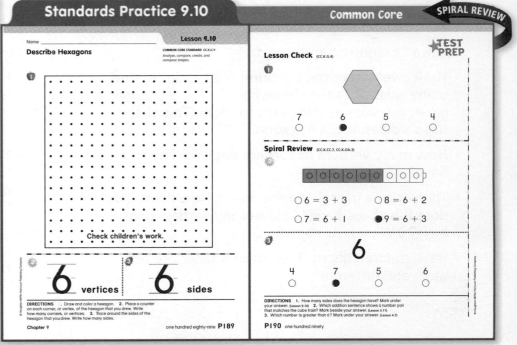

Standards Practice 9.10

Common Core

SPIRAL REVIEW

Name _____
Describe Hexagons

COMMON CORE STANDARD CC.K.G.4
Analyze, compare, create, and compose shapes.

Check children's work.

6 vertices   **6** sides

DIRECTIONS 1. Draw and color a hexagon. 2. Place a counter on each corner, or vertex, of the hexagon that you drew. Write how many corners, or vertices. 3. Trace around the sides of the hexagon that you drew. Write how many sides.

Chapter 9

one hundred eighty-nine **P189**

Lesson Check (CC.K.G.4)

TEST PREP

7   6   5   4
○   ●   ○   ○

Spiral Review (CC.K.CC.7, CC.K.OA.3)

○ 6 = 3 + 3   ○ 8 = 6 + 2
○ 7 = 6 + 1   ● 9 = 6 + 3

6

4   7   5   6
○   ○   ○   ○

DIRECTIONS 1. How many sides does the hexagon have? Mark under your answer. (Lesson 9.10) 2. Which addition sentence shows a number pair that matches the cube train? Mark beside your answer. (Lesson 5.11) 3. Which number is greater than 6? Mark under your answer. (Lesson 4.7)

P190 one hundred ninety

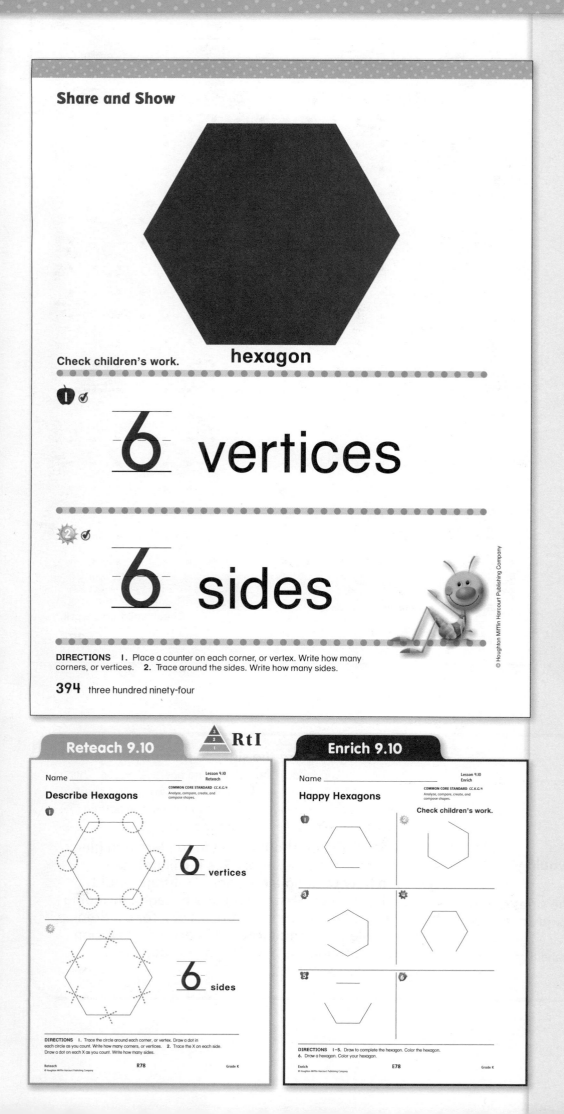

Share and Show

hexagon

Check children's work.

❶ ✓

6 vertices

❷ ✓

6 sides

© Houghton Mifflin Harcourt Publishing Company

DIRECTIONS 1. Place a counter on each corner, or vertex. Write how many corners, or vertices. 2. Trace around the sides. Write how many sides.

394 three hundred ninety-four

Reteach 9.10 ▲RtI

Name _____

Describe Hexagons

Lesson 9.10
Reteach

COMMON CORE STANDARD CC.K.G.4
Analyze, compare, create, and compose shapes.

❶

6 vertices

6 sides

DIRECTIONS 1. Trace the circle around each corner, or vertex. Draw a dot in each circle as you count. Write how many corners, or vertices. 2. Trace the X on each side. Draw a dot on each X as you count. Write how many sides.

Reteach   R78   Grade K
© Houghton Mifflin Harcourt Publishing Company

Enrich 9.10

Name _____

Happy Hexagons

Lesson 9.10
Enrich

COMMON CORE STANDARD CC.K.G.4
Analyze, compare, create, and compose shapes.

Check children's work.

❶   ✦

❸   ❖

❺   ❻

DIRECTIONS 1–5. Draw to complete the hexagon. Color the hexagon. 6. Draw a hexagon. Color your hexagon.

Enrich   E78   Grade K
© Houghton Mifflin Harcourt Publishing Company

---

③ PRACTICE Math Board

▶ **Share and Show** • **Guided Practice**

Materials two-color counters

Call attention to the hexagon at the top of the page. Have children trace around the hexagon with a finger. Then have children use counters to complete the page.

• **Place a counter on each corner, or vertex. How many vertices do you see?** 6 **Write the number.**

Have children remove the counters.

• **Trace around each side. What number will you write?** 6

Read the completed lines with children: **six vertices, six sides.** Explain that those words describe a hexagon.

• **This hexagon has the same number of sides and vertices. What is that number?** 6

Use Exercises 1 and 2 for **Quick Check.**

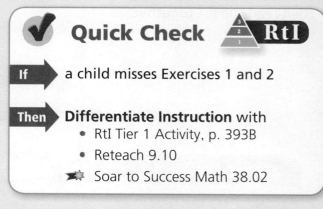

✓ **Quick Check** ▲RtI

If → a child misses Exercises 1 and 2

Then → **Differentiate Instruction** with
• RtI Tier 1 Activity, p. 393B
• Reteach 9.10
• Soar to Success Math 38.02

⚠ **COMMON ERRORS**

Error Children may not be able to tell the difference between sides and vertices.

Example Children count sides and vertices together when counting sides.

Springboard to Learning Have children draw a circle on each vertex, or corner, and draw an X on each side. They can count each X to find the number of sides.

► More Practice

Call attention to the dotted grid on the page. Read the directions.

- **What do you need to know to draw a hexagon?** I need to know that a hexagon has six sides and six vertices.

Show children how to draw a hexagon on the grid using six dots as the six vertices. Circle any six dots but be sure that no set of three dots are in a row. Then connect the six vertices. Have children draw a hexagon. Explain that it can be any size they choose.

Because this grid is a square grid, hexagons drawn on it will not be regular. Assure children that as long as their shapes have six connected sides, the shapes are hexagons.

After children complete a hexagon, have them count the vertices to make sure that there are six. Then have children color the hexagon.

H.O.T. Problem Make a smaller hexagon than the one you drew. Discuss how children chose the vertices to make a smaller hexagon.

Go Deeper (MATHEMATICAL PRACTICES)

Ask children to think of things that are shaped like hexagons. Make a list with the children. Then read the list together.

Name _____

③

© Houghton Mifflin Harcourt Publishing Company

DIRECTIONS 3. Draw and color a hexagon.

Check children's work.

Chapter 9 • Lesson 10

three hundred ninety-five **395**

Extend the Math | Activity

Make a Hexagon

Materials glue, paper, chenille stems or straws cut into equal pieces (6 per child)

Investigate Have children make a hexagon.
Math Talk

- **If you wanted to build a hexagon what would you need?** Possible answer: six things to use as sides
- **Do you think you should start by gluing the sides down one at a time as you make the hexagon? Explain.** Possible answer: I would not start by gluing. I would make the hexagon first so I can make sure all the sides are in the right place and that all the sides touch each other before I glue.

- **How can you place the sides to make a hexagon?** Possible answer: I would start by putting one side on top. Then I would put two sides going down and out. Next I would put two more sides going down and in. Last I would put the bottom side and make sure it touches the last two sides.

Summarize Children should be able to place and glue six pieces to make a hexagon. See if children can verbalize how to build a hexagon. Children should demonstrate an understanding of a hexagon including how many sides and vertices it has. Look for children who are able to communicate the parts of a hexagon and why the shape they made is a hexagon.

PROBLEM SOLVING

Check children's work.

DIRECTIONS I have 6 sides and 6 vertices. What shape am I? Draw the shape. Tell a friend the name of the shape.

HOME ACTIVITY • Have your child describe a hexagon.

396 three hundred ninety-six

FOR MORE PRACTICE: Standards Practice Book, pp. P189–P190

© Houghton Mifflin Harcourt Publishing Company

▶ **Problem Solving**

Read the riddle for the children. Ask children to explain how they will answer the riddle.

- **What shape has six sides?** a hexagon
- **What shape has six vertices?** a hexagon
- **How would you describe a hexagon?** A hexagon has six straight sides and six vertices.

Remind children to use six sides and six vertices as they draw the hexagon.

Invite children to tell a friend about their drawing. Have children compare the number of sides in their hexagons. Then have them compare the number of vertices in their hexagons.

4 SUMMARIZE

Essential Question

How can you describe hexagons? A hexagon is a shape with six sides and six vertices.

Differentiated Instruction **INDEPENDENT ACTIVITIES**

Grab-and-Go!
Differentiated Centers Kit

Literature
I Know Shapes
Children read the book and identify circles, squares, rectangles, and triangles.

Games
Number Picture
Children identify and color two-dimensional shapes to complete a picture.

Digital Path

- Animated Math Models
- iTools
- HMH Mega Math
- Soar to Success Math
- eStudent Edition

Hands On: Algebra • Compare Two-Dimensional Shapes

LESSON AT A GLANCE

Common Core Standard
Analyze, compare, create, and compose shapes.
CC.K.G.4 Analyze and compare two- and three-dimensional shapes, in different sizes and orientations, using informal language to describe their similarities, differences, parts (e.g., number of sides and vertices/"corners") and other attributes (e.g., having sides of equal length).

Also CC.K.G.2

Lesson Objective
Use the words *alike* and *different* to compare two-dimensional shapes by attributes.

Essential Question
How can you use the words *alike* and *different* to compare two-dimensional shapes?

Vocabulary alike, different

Materials
MathBoard, two-dimensional shapes

Digital Path

☑ **Animated Math Models**   i**T** *i***Tools: Counters**

i**T** *i***Tools: Geometry**   〽 **HMH Mega Math**

COMMON CORE PROFESSIONAL DEVELOPMENT

Building Mathematical Practices

CC.K–12.MP.7 Look for and make use of structure.

When comparing shapes, children should be able to find structure. Children learn that a shape may be round and curved or it may have a certain number of sides and vertices.

As children learn more shapes they can use structure to know that to identify the shape they should look at the attributes. When children learn about more shapes in later grades they will be looking beyond the number of sides and vertices to parallel sides, for example.

It is important children understand that shapes have a certain structure and it is this structure that defines what shape it is. They can use their knowledge of structure to solve problems. They should see two sides that meet and know they can make a triangle by adding one more side.

Daily Routines
Math Board

Common Core

SPIRAL REVIEW

Problem of the Day
eTransparency 9.11

Number of the Day Read each number.

7 14 19

Tell the number that comes before each number when you count.

Tell the number that comes after each number when you count.

6, 8; 13, 15; 18, 20
Have children read each number. Have them tell the number that comes before and after when counting.

Vocabulary Builder

Alike, Different

Draw a triangle, rectangle, square, hexagon, and circle. Have children name each one. Point to the triangle and the rectangle.

- **How are these shapes alike?** Possible answer: They have straight sides. **How are these shapes different?** Possible answer: The triangle has three sides and the rectangle has four sides.

Point to the circle and the hexagon.

- **How are these shapes alike?** Possible answer: They are both flat shapes. **How are these shapes different?** Possible answer: The hexagon has straight sides and the circle is curved.

Have volunteers take turns selecting two different shapes and ask a question using *alike* or *different*.

Differentiated Instruction Activities

ELL Language Support
🕐 Auditory / Visual
Small Group

Strategy: Describe

Materials two-dimensional shapes

Children can demonstrate their understanding by describing in words what they have done.

- Place a handful of shapes on the table.
- Have children sort the shapes by the number of sides. As they sort, have them explain what they are doing with each shape.
- Once groups are sorted, have children describe how each group is alike or different.

See **ELL** Activity Guide for leveled activities.

Enrich
🕐 Visual
Individuals

Materials paper, paint

Hand each child two pieces of paper and paint. Invite children to paint two pictures, one using two alike shapes and one using two different shapes. Ideas include painting a tree, a house, a hat, or a robot.

- Have children label each painting *Alike* or *Different*.

RtI Response to Intervention

Reteach Tier 1
🕐 Visual / Kinesthetic
Whole Class / Small Group

Materials paper divided in half and labeled *alike* and *different*, Two-Dimensional Shapes (see *eTeacher Resources*)

Give each child in the group one shape. Have children name their shapes.

- Have the group sort the shapes into two sets by number of sides.
- Have children use the words *alike* and *different* to describe the shapes in the sets.

Repeat having children select different shapes for each group.

Tier 2
🕐 Visual / Kinesthetic
Small Group

Materials Two-Dimensional Shapes (see *eTeacher Resources*)

Show children triangles and rectangles. Have them help you sort the shapes into two sets by the number of sides.

- Discuss how these shapes are different. Possible answer: The triangles have three sides and the rectangles have four sides.
- Show children squares and rectangles that are not squares. Discuss how these shapes are alike. They all have four sides
- Repeat the activity using a different attribute such as: number of vertices, curved or not curved, six sides or not six sides.

1 ENGAGE

Materials paper bag, assorted two-dimensional shapes

Access Prior Knowledge Hold up a paper bag filled with shapes. Ask children to guess what is inside the bag.

Have volunteers take turns reaching inside and pulling out one shape at time, naming the shape, and telling something about the shape.

2 TEACH and TALK   GO Online   Animated Math Models

▶ **Listen and Draw**   MATHEMATICAL PRACTICES

Read aloud this problem as children listen.

Erica wants to color some shapes. She wants to color shapes with four vertices and four sides green. She will use blue to color shapes with curves. She will color shapes with three sides and three vertices red. What shapes will be green? Blue? Red?

Have children locate the worms at the top of the page and review the words *vertex, curve,* and *side.*

As you ask the questions below encourage children to use the words from the top of the page for their answers.

- **How are the rectangle and square *alike*?**
  Possible answers: They are alike because both have four sides and four corners or vertices. They are both rectangles.

Discuss that both shapes are rectangles, but a square is a special type of rectangle because it has four sides of equal length.

- **Why is a square a special type of rectangle?**
  Possible answer: A square has four sides of equal length.

Have children compare the triangle and circle.

- **How are the triangle and circle alike?** Possible answer: They are alike because they are both closed shapes.

- **How are they different?** Possible answer: They are different because the triangle has straight sides and the circle has curves.

Read the directions explaining how to color the shapes. Pause as children complete each step.

Reread the problem.

- **What shapes will Erica color green?** rectangles
  blue? circles **red?** triangles

MATHEMATICAL PRACTICES **Describe how shapes are alike. How are they different?**

CC.K.G.4 Analyze and compare two-and three-dimensional shapes, in different sizes and orientations, using informal language to describe their similarities, differences, parts (e.g., number of sides and vertices/"corners") and other attributes (e.g., having sides of equal length)

COMMON CORE

Name _____

Algebra • Compare Two-Dimensional Shapes

HANDS ON
Lesson 9.11

COMMON CORE STANDARD CC.K.G.4
Analyze, compare, create, and compose shapes.

Essential Question How can you use the words *alike* and *different* to compare two-dimensional shapes?

Listen and Draw

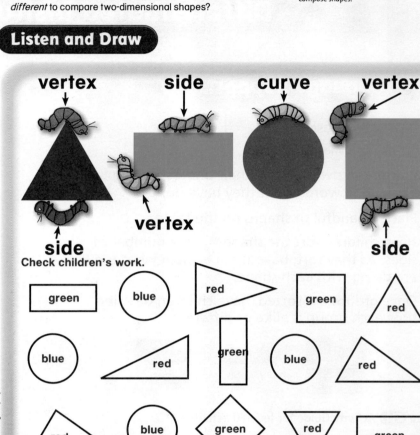

Check children's work.

DIRECTIONS Look at the worms and the shapes. Use the words *alike* and *different* to compare the shapes. Use green to color the shapes with four vertices and four sides. Use blue to color the shapes with curves. Use red to color the shapes with three vertices and three sides.

Chapter 9 • Lesson 11   three hundred ninety-seven **397**

Standards Practice 9.11

Common Core   SPIRAL REVIEW

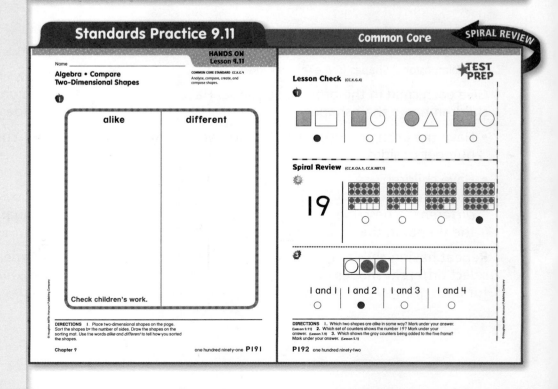

Name _____

Algebra • Compare Two-Dimensional Shapes

HANDS ON
Lesson 9.11

COMMON CORE STANDARD CC.K.G.4
Analyze, compare, create, and compose shapes.

❶

alike	different

Check children's work.

DIRECTIONS 1. Place two-dimensional shapes on the page. Sort the shapes by the number of sides. Draw the shapes on the sorting mat. Use the words *alike* and *different* to tell how you sorted the shapes.

Chapter 9   one hundred ninety-one **P191**

Lesson Check (CC.K.G.4)   ★TEST PREP

❶

Spiral Review (CC.K.OA.1, CC.K.NBT.1)

19

❸

| I and I | I and 2 | I and 3 | I and 4 |

DIRECTIONS 1. Which two shapes are alike in some way? Mark under your answer. (Lesson 9.11) 2. Which set of counters shows the number 19? Mark under your answer. (Lesson 7.9) 3. Which shows the gray counters being added to the five frame? Mark under your answer. (Lesson 5.1)

P192 one hundred ninety-two

Share and Show

1

alike	different

Check children's work.

DIRECTIONS **1.** Place two-dimensional shapes on the page. Sort the shapes by the number of vertices. Draw the shapes on the sorting mat. Use the words *alike* and *different* to tell how you sorted the shapes.

398 three hundred ninety-eight

Reteach 9.11 RtI

Name _____ Lesson 9.11 Reteach

Algebra • Compare Two-Dimensional Shapes COMMON CORE STANDARD CC.K.G.4 Analyze, compare, create, and compose shapes.

1

alike	different

DIRECTIONS **1.** Sort two-dimensional shapes by number of vertices as shown. Trace the shapes that have four vertices. Tell a friend why they are alike. Trace the other shapes. Tell a friend why they are different.

Reteach   R79   Grade K
© Houghton Mifflin Harcourt Publishing Company

Enrich 9.11

Name _____ Lesson 9.11 Enrich

Sort Spilled Shapes COMMON CORE STANDARD CC.K.G.4 Analyze, compare, create, and compose shapes.

1

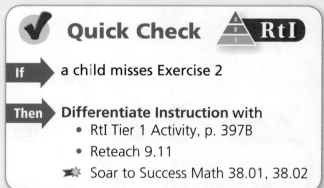

curved	3 sides
4 sides	6 vertices

DIRECTIONS **1.** Sort the shapes that have spilled out of the basket. Draw and color the shapes in the correct sorting box.

Enrich   E79   Grade K
© Houghton Mifflin Harcourt Publishing Company

---

3 **PRACTICE** [Math Board]

▶ **Share and Show** • **Guided Practice**

Materials Two-Dimensional shapes (see *eTeacher Resources*)

Direct children's attention to the page and read the labels. Explain that they are going to sort shapes into two sets, shapes that are *alike* and shapes that are *different* than the alike ones.

Have each child choose the number of vertices he or she wants to sort by for the *alike* set.

Explain that the *different* set will be shapes that do not have that number of vertices.

- **Put all the shapes that have the number of vertices you picked in the *alike* set.**
- **Put all the shapes that do not have the number of vertices you picked in the *different* set.**

After children sort the shapes, have them draw (or trace) the shapes on the sorting mat. Hold a discussion of how children sorted, and emphasize using the words *alike* and *different*.

Use Exercise 2 for **Quick Check**.

> ✔ **Quick Check** RtI
>
> **If** → a child misses Exercise 2
>
> **Then** → **Differentiate Instruction** with
> - RtI Tier 1 Activity, p. 397B
> - Reteach 9.11
> - Soar to Success Math 38.01, 38.02

> ⚠ **COMMON ERRORS**
>
> **Error** Children may have difficulty deciding what shapes are *alike*.
>
> **Example** Children may have a sorting rule of three vertices but sort both triangles and squares as *alike*.
>
> **Springboard to Learning** Have children count the vertices for each shape and compare that number to the sorting rule. The numbers must be the same for the shapes to be *alike*.

Lesson 9.11 **398**

▶ More Practice

- Choose a way to sort for the number of sides. Shapes with that number of sides will be *alike*. Shapes with a different number of sides will be *different*.

Children will use two-dimensional shapes to sort on the mat by the number of sides each child chooses as his or her way to sort.

- Sort the shapes by the way you picked. Compare the number of sides to check your work.

- **Compare the shapes. How are they alike?**
Possible answer: They have the same number of sides.
How are they different? Possible answer: They have different numbers of sides and vertices.

H.O.T. Problem Which shape that you know has two names? a square, it is also a rectangle

Go Deeper MATHEMATICAL PRACTICES

Present children with a set of shapes that includes squares, rectangles that are not squares, and triangles. Ask children to tell which shapes do not belong and why. triangles Draw a square sitting on a vertex and ask if it belongs and why. Yes, it has four sides. **Repeat with other four-sided shapes that are not rectangles.**

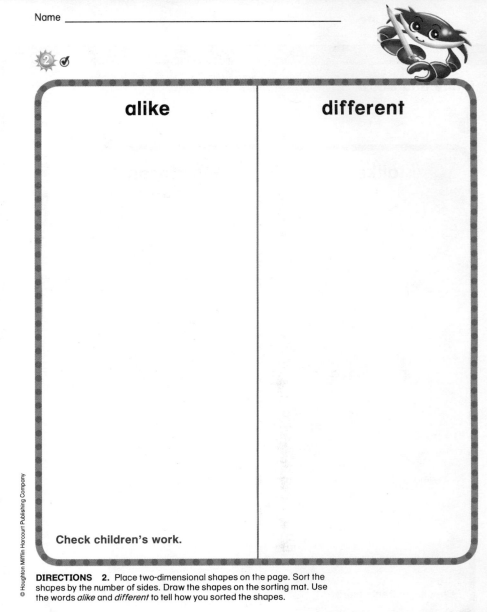

Name _____

alike	different

Check children's work.

© Houghton Mifflin Harcourt Publishing Company

DIRECTIONS 2. Place two-dimensional shapes on the page. Sort the shapes by the number of sides. Draw the shapes on the sorting mat. Use the words *alike* and *different* to tell how you sorted the shapes.

Chapter 9 • Lesson 11   three hundred ninety-nine **399**

Cross-Curricular   SCIENCE

Materials drawing paper, crayons

- Ask children to name their favorite animals and tell what they know about them. Compare two animals, noting how they are alike or different.

- Have children suggest how to draw the animal using shapes and draw it for them on the chalkboard.

- After the drawing is completed, have children identify the shapes that were used.

- Then give children drawing paper and invite them to draw an animal, real or not, that is made with shapes.

SOCIAL STUDIES

Materials American flag

- Display an American flag. Discuss how it is a symbol for the United States. Tell children that people like to wave flags, especially on days like July 4th, Memorial Day, and Flag Day.

- Ask children to identify the flag's two long sides and two short sides.

- **What shape is an American flag if it has two long sides and two short sides?** a rectangle

- Then call attention to other parts of the flag, such as the blue background box, stripes, and stars.

- **What parts of the flag are *alike*?** stripes, stars

- **How are the stripes *different*?** Possible answers: color and length

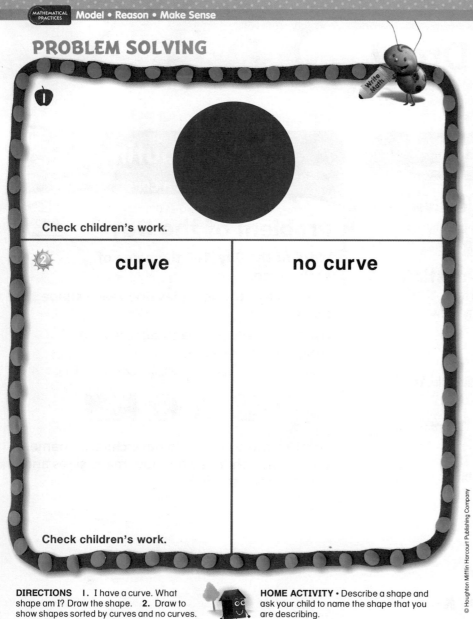

PROBLEM SOLVING

Model • Reason • Make Sense

1

Check children's work.

2 | **curve** | **no curve** |

Check children's work.

DIRECTIONS 1. I have a curve. What shape am I? Draw the shape. **2.** Draw to show shapes sorted by curves and no curves.

HOME ACTIVITY · Describe a shape and ask your child to name the shape that you are describing.

400 four hundred

FOR MORE PRACTICE:
Standards Practice Book, pp. P191–P192

© Houghton Mifflin Harcourt Publishing Company

▶ **Problem Solving** MATHEMATICAL PRACTICES

Read the riddle for Exercise 1. Ask children to explain how they will answer the riddle.

- **What shape can you name that is curved?** a circle
- **What shape will you draw for Exercise 1?** a circle

Read the directions for Exercise 2.

- **What shape is curved?** a circle **Draw a circle on the left side of the mat.**
- **What shapes have no curves?** a triangle, a square, a hexagon, and a rectangle **What shapes will you draw on the right side of the sorting mat?** triangle, square, hexagon, rectangle

Have children share their drawings with a partner. Have them name the shapes in each set.

4 SUMMARIZE MATHEMATICAL PRACTICES

Essential Question

How can you use the words *alike* and *different* to compare two-dimensional shapes?
I can choose a number of sides or vertices and make a set of shapes with that number and label it *alike*. I can put all the other shapes in another set and label it *different*.

Differentiated Instruction

INDEPENDENT ACTIVITIES

Grab-and-Go!™
Differentiated Centers Kit

Activities
Same Game

Children complete the purple Activity Card 3 by sorting objects by shape.

Literature
Hippo and Fox
Sort Socks

Children read the book and learn about classifying socks into different categories.

Games
Number Picture

Children identify and color two-dimensional shapes to complete a picture.

Digital Path

- ☑ Animated Math Models
- *i*T *i*Tools
- MM HMH Mega Math
- ☆ Soar to Success Math
- GO eStudent Edition

Lesson 9.11 400

Problem Solving • Draw to Join Shapes

LESSON AT A GLANCE

Common Core Standard
Analyze, compare, create, and compose shapes.
CC.K.G.6 Compose simple shapes to form larger shapes.

Lesson Objective
Solve problems by using the strategy *draw a picture*.

Essential Question
How can you solve problems using the strategy *draw a picture*?

Materials
MathBoard, Pattern Blocks

Digital Path
- 📺 Animated Math Models
- 🔺 HMH Mega Math
- 📱 eStudent Edition

Daily Routines
Common Core

SPIRAL REVIEW

eTransparency 9.12

Problem of the Day

Word of the Day Tell the name of each shape.

How many straight sides does each shape have?

Use the words *alike* and *different* to compare two shapes.

hexagon, 6; square, 4; triangle, 3; circle, 0; rectangle, 4

Point to the shapes and have children name them. Have children tell how many sides and vertices each shape has.

COMMON CORE MATHEMATICAL PRACTICES
Using Pattern Blocks

Most pattern blocks have sides that are the same length. The longest side of the trapezoid block is twice the length of its other sides. This feature will be useful as children combine the blocks to make more complex shapes.

In some cases, there is more than one way to combine shapes to fill the outline of another shape. For example, three green triangles or a triangle and a blue rhombus will fill the outline of a red trapezoid. A hexagon block's outline may be filled with six triangles; two trapezoids; three blue rhombuses; two blue rhombuses and two triangles; one trapezoid and three triangles; or one trapezoid, one triangle, and one blue rhombus.

In this lesson, children will explore using pattern blocks to compose other shapes.

Hexagon **Square** **Rhombus**

Triangle **Rhombus** **Trapezoid**

Differentiated Instruction Activities

ELL Language Support
Visual / Auditory
Small Group

Strategy: Model Language

Materials Pattern Blocks

Children can understand language by making connections between new information and prior knowledge.

- Have each child trace a hexagon shape. Then have each child use other blocks to fill in the outline of the hexagon.

- After they have filled in the shape, have children describe the shapes they joined to create the hexagon.

Repeat the activity with another shape if time permits.

See **ELL** Activity Guide for leveled activities.

Enrich
Visual
Individual / Partners

Materials Pattern Blocks, crayons, paper

Hand children a sheet of paper with three hexagons outlined on it. Have children choose one pattern block and trace its shape attached to each of the three hexagons.

- Children should switch papers with a partner and use pattern blocks to fill in the shape three different ways. They can outline the blocks and color in the traced shapes.

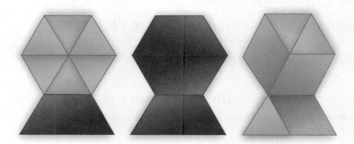

▲ RtI Response to Intervention

Reteach Tier 1
Kinesthetic / Visual / Verbal
Whole Class / Small Group

Materials squares, right triangles, rectangles that are not square

Have children join four squares to make one larger shape. **What shape did you make?** Possible answer: a large square **How did you make it?** Possible answer: I joined four small squares.

- Have children draw a picture to show how they joined shapes to make a larger shape.

Repeat this with other shapes to form one large triangle and one large rectangle.

Tier 2
Kinesthetic / Visual
Small Group

Materials Pattern Blocks

Tell children they can join shapes to make a shape that is the same as the red shape (trapezoid).

Give each child a red shape and see what shapes he or she can join to cover the shape exactly.

- When they are ready, have children turn to a friend and compare solutions.

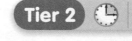

Repeat for a yellow hexagon and a blue shape (rhombus).

1 ENGAGE

Materials Pattern Blocks, paper bag

Access Prior Knowledge Place the triangles, squares, and hexagons in a bag. Have children take turns picking a pattern block, and describing it.

- **How many sides does the shape have?**
  Answers should reflect shapes.

- **How many vertices does the shape have?**
  Answers should reflect shapes.

2 TEACH and TALK

▶ **Unlock the Problem**

Materials Pattern Blocks

Read aloud this problem as children listen.

Lauren only has triangles. She wants to make other shapes. How can she make other shapes by joining triangles?

Help children use their triangle pattern blocks to fill in the outlines on the page and then draw and color the pattern blocks that they use.

- **Fill in the red shape with green triangles. How many did you use?** 2 **Trace and color the triangles.**

- **Fill in the blue shape with green triangles. How many did you use?** 3 **Draw and color the triangles.**

- **Fill in the hexagon at the bottom of the page with green triangles. How many did you use?** 6 **Draw and color the triangles.**

Reread the problem.

- **How can Lauren make a shape like the red shape?** She can join two triangles.

- **How can she make a shape like the blue shape?** She can join three triangles.

- **How can she make a hexagon?** She can join six triangles.

Name _____

Problem Solving • Draw to Join Shapes

Essential Question How can you solve problems using the strategy *draw a picture*?

PROBLEM SOLVING
Lesson **9.12**

COMMON CORE STANDARD CC.K.G.6
Analyze, compare, create, and compose shapes.

Unlock the Problem

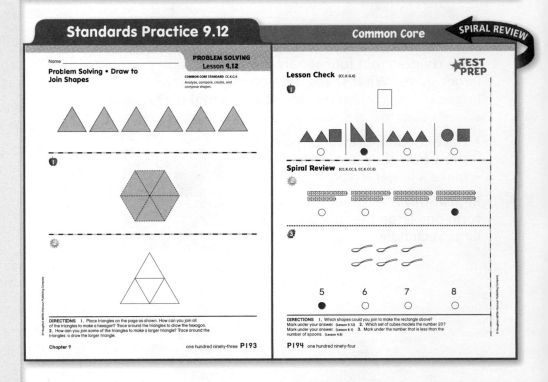

DIRECTIONS How can you join triangles to make the shapes? Draw and color the triangles.

Chapter 9 · Lesson 12   four hundred one **401**

Standards Practice 9.12   **Common Core**   SPIRAL REVIEW

Name _____
Problem Solving • Draw to Join Shapes

COMMON CORE STANDARD CC.K.G.6
Analyze, compare, create, and compose shapes.

Lesson Check (CC.K.G.6)

Spiral Review (CC.K.CC.5, CC.K.CC.6)

5   6   7   8

DIRECTIONS 1. Place triangles on the page as shown. How can you join all of the triangles to make a hexagon? Trace around the triangles to draw the hexagon. 2. How can you join some of the triangles to make a larger triangle? Trace around the triangles o draw the larger triangle.

Chapter 9   one hundred ninety-three **P193**

DIRECTIONS 1. Which shapes could you join to make the rectangle above? Mark under your answer. (Lesson 9.12) 2. Which set of cubes models the number 20? Mark under your answer. (Lesson 8.1) 3. Mark under the number that is less than the number of spoons. (Lesson 4.4)

P194 one hundred ninety-four

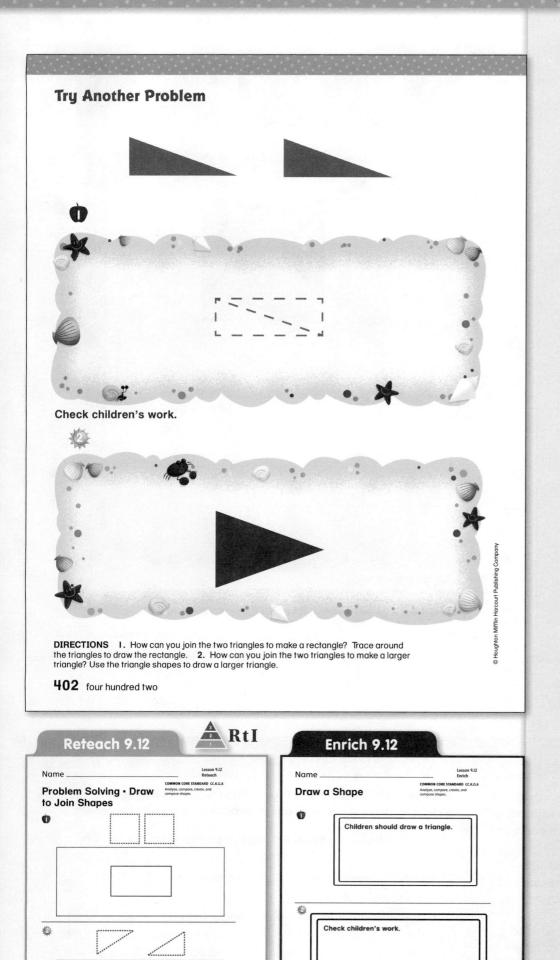

Try Another Problem

1

Check children's work.

2

DIRECTIONS **1.** How can you join the two triangles to make a rectangle? Trace around the triangles to draw the rectangle. **2.** How can you join the two triangles to make a larger triangle? Use the triangle shapes to draw a larger triangle.

402 four hundred two

© Houghton Mifflin Harcourt Publishing Company

▶ **Try Another Problem**

Materials Two-Dimensional shapes (see *eTeacher Resources*)

Discuss how larger shapes can be made by joining smaller shapes.

- **What shapes are at the top of the page?** triangles
- **Look at the triangles. Place the triangles to make the rectangle. Trace around the triangles.**

Explain and demonstrate how a triangle can be flipped or turned to make a shape.

- **Now you will join the two triangles to make the larger triangle. Trace around the triangles.**

Remind children they may need to flip or turn the triangles to make the larger one.

Use Exercise 4 for **Quick Check.**

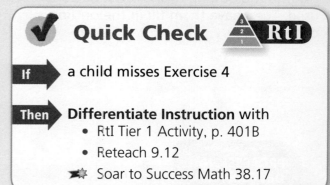

✔ **Quick Check** ▲ RtI

If ▶ a child misses Exercise 4

Then ▶ **Differentiate Instruction** with
- RtI Tier 1 Activity, p. 401B
- Reteach 9.12
- ✦ Soar to Success Math 38.17

⚠ **COMMON ERRORS**

Error Children do not understand how to use smaller shapes to make a bigger shape.

Example Children cannot make a larger triangle.

Springboard to Learning Tell children to join two triangles together in different ways until the shape they form is another triangle. Demonstrate how to flip and turn the shapes to see all possible ways to join them.

③ PRACTICE

▶ **Share and Show** • Guided Practice

Make sure children have five squares to use.

- **Think how you can join some or all of the square shapes to make a larger square.**

For Exercise 3, have children trace around the four square shapes to draw the large square.

Discuss whether it is possible to make a square using all five squares. Help children conclude that it is not possible.

Call attention to Exercise 4. Tell children to use some or all of the square shapes to make a rectangle. Have children trace around the square shapes. Discuss how there are many possible ways to make the shape.

H.O.T. Problem Have children choose three pattern blocks and place them next to each other with at least one side touching. Have children trace the outline of the three pattern blocks.

- **How many sides and vertices are in the shape you made?** Check children's work.

Go Deeper MATHEMATICAL PRACTICES

Have children trade papers and have a partner color in the outline to show the pattern blocks used. Then have them fill in the outline a different way.

Name _____

Share and Show

③

④ ✓

Check children's work.
DIRECTIONS 3. How can you join some of the squares to make a larger square? Use the square shapes to draw a larger square. 4. How can you join some or all of the squares to make a rectangle? Use the square shapes to draw a rectangle.

Chapter 9 • Lesson 12   four hundred three **403**

© Houghton Mifflin Harcourt Publishing Company

COMMON CORE
PROFESSIONAL DEVELOPMENT

Mathematical Practices in Your Classroom

CC.K–12.MP.3 Construct viable arguments and critique the reasoning of others. Being able to create a reasonable argument or evaluate another person's argument is an important mathematical skill.

- Children are able to make valid arguments by building a logical progression of statements to explain their reasoning. For example, I know it is a triangle because it has three sides and three vertices.
- They are able to take apart situations into smaller parts to analyze them. For example, I know this shape is a rectangle because it has four sides and four vertices. It is also a square because the sides are all of equal length.
- They should also be able to justify their conclusions and communicate them precisely to others, as well as be able to respond to arguments of others.

A shape with four sides and four vertices is shown. Ashley says it is a rectangle. Drew says it is a square. Explain who is probably correct.

- **How would you begin solving this problem?** I would think of shapes with four sides and four vertices.
- **Which shapes have four sides and four vertices?** squares and other rectangles
- **Can you know for sure which child is correct?** There is no way to know for sure without seeing the shape because it could be either shape or a new shape we do not know about with four sides and four vertices.
- **Does only one child have to be correct? Explain.** They both can be correct because if the shape is a square then it can also be called a rectangle because a square is a special kind of rectangle.

On Your Own

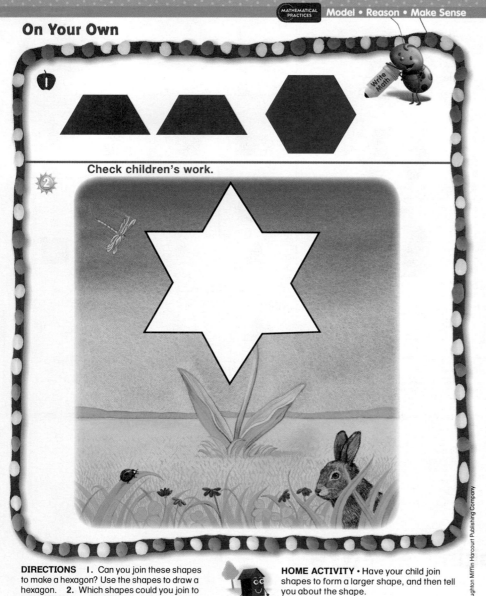

①

② Check children's work.

DIRECTIONS **1.** Can you join these shapes to make a hexagon? Use the shapes to draw a hexagon. **2.** Which shapes could you join to make the larger shape? Draw and color to show the shapes you used.

HOME ACTIVITY • Have your child join shapes to form a larger shape, and then tell you about the shape.

404 four hundred four

FOR EXTRA PRACTICE:
Standards Practice Book, p. P196

FOR MORE PRACTICE:
Standards Practice Book, pp. P193–P194

© Houghton Mifflin Harcourt Publishing Company

▶ **On Your Own**

Read the question. Ask children to explain how they will solve the problem.

Explain that they may need to rotate one of these shapes a different way to make the hexagon (turning one to join the other on a different side to make the hexagon).

Which shapes can you use to fill the outline in Exercise 2? Possible answer: a hexagon and triangles **You may need to turn and move the shapes to fill the outline. Draw to show how you filled the outline.**

Have children share their drawings with the class. Discuss how there are many different ways to make the shape on the page.

Portfolio You may suggest that children place the completed On Your Own page in their portfolios.

❹ SUMMARIZE MATHEMATICAL PRACTICES

Essential Question

How can you solve problems using the strategy *draw a picture*? I can join different shapes to form new shapes, and then draw the shapes to solve the problem.

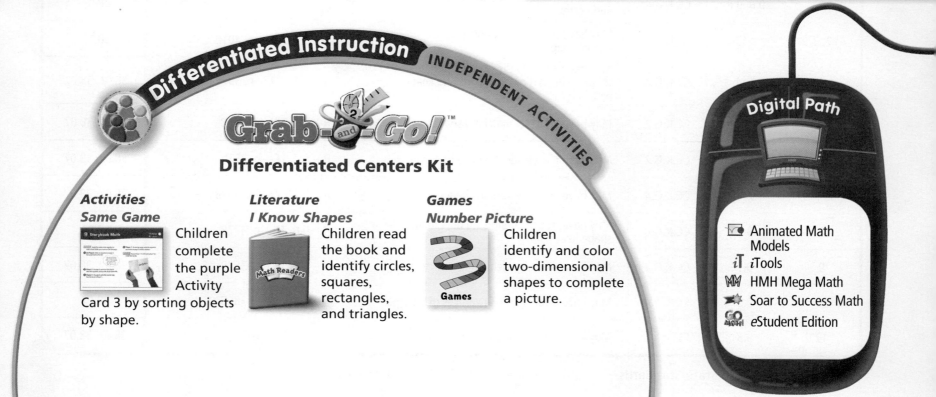

Differentiated Instruction INDEPENDENT ACTIVITIES

Grab-and-Go!™
Differentiated Centers Kit

Activities
Same Game
Children complete the purple Activity Card 3 by sorting objects by shape.

Literature
I Know Shapes
Children read the book and identify circles, squares, rectangles, and triangles.

Games
Number Picture
Children identify and color two-dimensional shapes to complete a picture.

Digital Path

- Animated Math Models
- iT iTools
- MM HMH Mega Math
- Soar to Success Math
- eStudent Edition

Lesson 9.12   404

Summative Assessment

Use the **Chapter 9 Review/Test** to assess children's progress in Chapter 9.

You may want to review with children the essential question for this chapter.

Chapter Essential Question

How can you identify, name, and describe two-dimensional shapes?

Ask the following questions to focus children's thinking:

- How can knowing the parts of two-dimensional shapes help you join shapes?
- How can knowing the number of sides and vertices of two-dimensional shapes help you identify shapes?

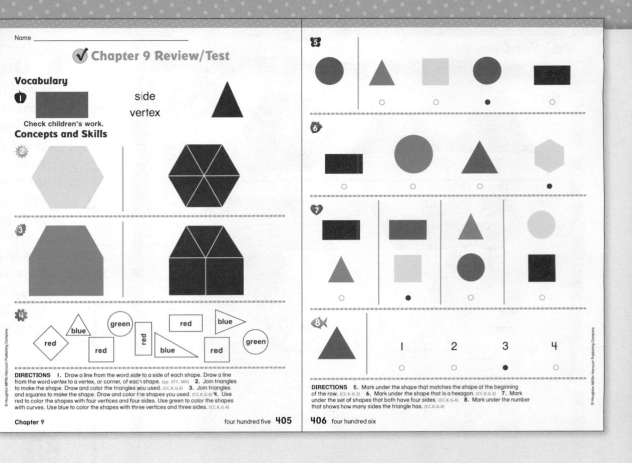

✓ Data-Driven Decision Making 🔺 RtI

Based on the results of the Chapter Review/Test use the following resources to review skills.

Item	Lesson	*CCSS	Common Error	Intervene With	Soar to Success Math
1	9.6, 9.8	CC.K.G.4	May have trouble understanding *side* and *vertex*	R—9.6, 9.8; TE—pp. 377B, 385B	38.02
2, 3	9.12	CC.K.G.6	May have difficulty identifying and joining shapes	R—9.12; TE—p. 401B	38.17
4	9.11	CC.K.G.4	May have difficulty differentiating between shapes with vertices and sides and shapes with curves	R—9.11; TE—p. 397B	38.01, 38.02
5	9.1	CC.K.G.2	May have difficulty matching shapes	R—9.1; TE—p. 357B	38.02, 38.07
6	9.7	CC.K.G.2	May have trouble identifying a hexagon	R—9.7; TE—p. 381B	38.02, 38.07
7, 11	9.11	CC.K.G.4	May have difficulty sorting shapes	R—9.11; TE—p. 397B	38.01, 38.02
8	9.6	CC.K.G.4	May have trouble identifying how many sides a shape has	R—9.6; TE—p. 377B	38.02
9	9.1	CC.K.G.2	May have difficulty identifying a circle	R—9.1; TE—p. 357B	38.02, 38.07
10	9.8	CC.K.G.4	May have trouble finding vertices of a shape	R—9.8; TE—p. 385B	38.02
12	9.3	CC.K.G.2	May have difficulty identifying a square	R—9.3; TE—p. 365B	38.02, 38.07

*CCSS—Common Core State Standards   Key: R—Reteach Book; TE—RtI Activities

Name _____

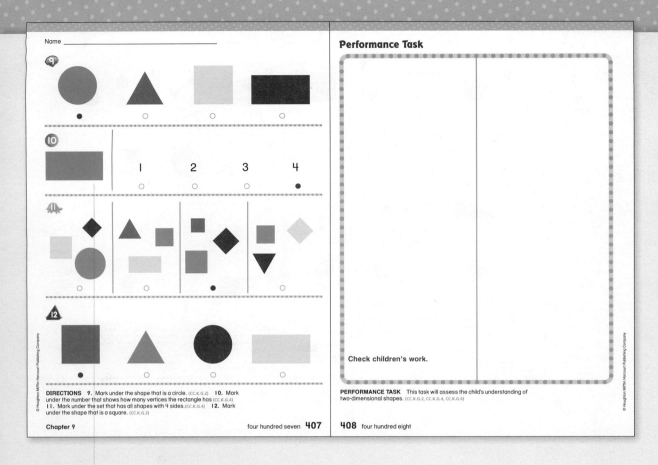

DIRECTIONS 9. Mark under the shape that is a circle. (CC.K.G.2) 10. Mark under the number that shows how many vertices the rectangle has (CC.K.G.4) 11. Mark under the set that has all shapes with 4 sides.(CC.K.G.4) 12. Mark under the shape that is a square. (CC.K.G.2)

Chapter 9   four hundred seven **407**

Performance Task

Check children's work.

PERFORMANCE TASK This task will assess the child's understanding of two-dimensional shapes. (CC.K.G.2, CC.K.G.4, CC.K.G.6)

408 four hundred eight

Performance Task
Extended Response

Objective Assess the understanding of two-dimensional shapes

Materials two-dimensional shapes

Listen and Do

Give each child a handful of shapes in various sizes and colors. Have them sort the shapes by a given attribute and name the shapes.

- **Sort the shapes into two sets, one with four sides and four vertices and one set of shapes that does not have four sides or four vertices. Draw the shapes to show how you sorted. Name these shapes.**

Use performance indicators, scoring rubric, and DOK level to evaluate conceptual understanding.

Performance Indicators

A child with a Level 2 paper:

_____ sorts rectangles and squares into a set of shapes with four sides and four vertices.

_____ identifies a triangle, a circle, and a hexagon as shapes without four sides and four vertices.

_____ draws a circle, square, triangle, rectangle, and hexagon.

_____ identifies and names two-dimensional shapes.

Depth of Knowledge

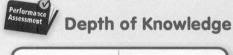

Performance Task	DOK Level
	2

Performance Task Scoring Rubric

2	**Generally accurate, complete, and clear:** All of the parts of the task are successfully completed. There is evidence of clear understanding of the key concepts and procedures. Child's work shows that all answers are correct or reasonable.
1	**Partially accurate:** Some of the tasks are successfully completed; other parts are attempted and their intent addressed, but they are not completed.
0	**Not accurate, complete, and clear:** No part of the task is completed with any success. There is little, if any, evidence that the child understands key concepts and procedures.

Performance Task may be used for portfolios.

Performance Assessment
Chapters 9–10

See *Assessment Guide* for Performance Tasks to be completed at the end of each critical area.

Chapter 9
Test

Summative Assessment

Use the **Chapter Test** to assess children's progress in Chapter 9.

Chapter tests are provided in multiple-choice and mixed-response format in the *Assessment Guide*.

 Chapter 9 Test is available online.

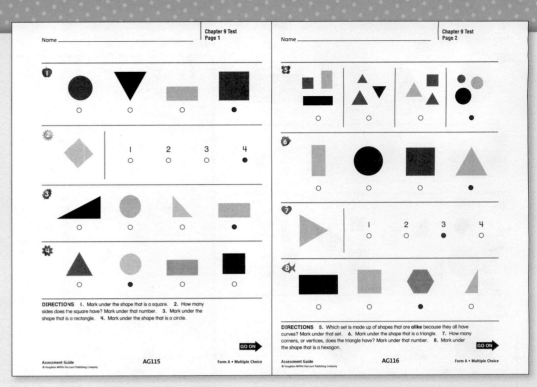

✓Data-Driven Decision Making ▲RtI

Item	Lesson	*CCSS	Common Error	Intervene With	Soar to Success Math
1	9.3	CC.K.G.2	May not correctly identify squares	R—9.3; **TE**—p. 365B	38.02, 38.07
2, 9	9.4	CC.K.G.4	May not correctly describe squares	R—9.4; **TE**—p. 369B	38.02
3	9.7	CC.K.G.2	May not correctly identify rectangles	R—9.7; **TE**—p. 381B	38.02, 38.07
4, 11	9.1	CC.K.G.2	May not correctly identify circles	R—9.1; **TE**—p. 357B	38.02, 38.07

*CCSS—Common Core State Standards   Key: **R**—Reteach Book; **TE**—RtI Activities

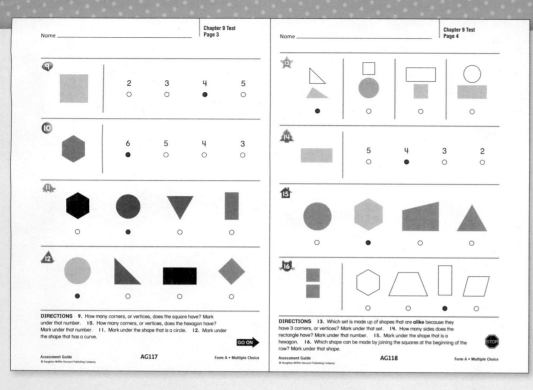

Chapter 9 Test

Portfolio Suggestions The portfolio represents the growth, talents, achievements, and reflections of the mathematics learner. Children might spend a short time selecting work samples for their portfolios and completing A Guide to My Math Portfolio from the *Assessment Guide*.

You may want to have children respond to the following questions:

• How do you think you did on this test?
• What would you like to learn more about?

For more information about how to organize, share, and evaluate portfolios, see the *Assessment Guide*.

✓ Data-Driven Decision Making ▲RtI

Item	Lesson	*CCSS	Common Error	Intervene With	Soar to Success Math
5, 13	9.11	CC.K.G.4	May have difficulty comparing attributes of two-dimensional shapes	R—9.11; TE—p. 397B	38.01, 38.02
6	9.5	CC.K.G.2	May not correctly identify triangles	R—9.5; TE—p. 373B	38.02, 38.07
7	9.6	CC.K.G.4	May not correctly describe triangles	R—9.6; TE—p. 377B	38.02
8, 15	9.9	CC.K.G.2	May not correctly identify hexagons	R—9.9; TE—p. 389B	38.02
10	9.10	CC.K.G.4	May not correctly describe hexagons	R—9.10; TE—p. 393B	38.02
12	9.2	CC.K.G.4	May not correctly describe circles	R—9.2; TE—p. 361B	38.02
14	9.8	CC.K.G.4	May not correctly describe rectangles	R—9.8; TE—p. 385B	38.02
16	9.12	CC.K.G.6	May not understand how to join two-dimensional shapes to make a larger two-dimensional shape	R—9.12; TE—p. 401B	38.17

***CCSS**—Common Core State Standards   **Key: R**—Reteach Book; **TE**—RtI Activities